www.physioex.com

Log on.

Tune in.

Succeed.

To help you succeed in physiology, your professor has arranged for you to enjoy access to a great media resource, PhysioEx 6.0: Laboratory Simulations in Physiology (www.physioex.com). You'll find that these resources will enhance your course materials and help you make the grade! A CD-ROM version of PhysioEx 6.0 is also packaged with this text.

What your system needs to use these media resources:

WINDOWS™
- 266 MHz Intel Pentium processor or greater
- Windows 98 or higher
- 64 MB Minimum RAM
- 1024 x 768 screen resolution
- Thousands of colors
- Browser:Internet Explorer 5.0 or higher; Netscape 7.0 or higher
- Plug-Ins: Flash Player 7, Acrobat Reader 7
- Internet Connection: 56k modem minimum for website

NOTE: Use of Netscape 6.0 and 6.1 are not recommended due to a known compatibility issue between Netscape 6.0 and 6.1 and the Flash and Shockwave plug-ins.

MACINTOSH™
- 266 MHz Minimum CPU
- OS 9.2.2, 10.2.6, 10.2.8, 10.3.5, 10.3.6, 10.3.7
- 64 MB Minimum RAM
- 1024 x 768 screen resolution
- Thousands of colors
- Browser: OS 9: Internet Explorer 5.1.7 or higher; OS X: Netscape 7.2 or higher, Internet Explorer 5.2.3 or higher
- Plug-Ins: Flash Player 7, Acrobat Reader 7
- Internet Connection: 56k modem minimum for website

NOTE: Use of Netscape 6.0 and 6.1 are not recommended due to a known compatibility issue between Netscape 6.0 and 6.1 and the Flash and Shockwave plug-ins.

Got technical questions?
For technical support, please visit http://247.aw.com and complete the appropriate online form. Email technical support is 24/7.

Here's your personal ticket to success:

How to log on to www.physioex.com:

1. Go to www.physioex.com.
2. Click "Register."
3. Scratch off the silver foil coating below to reveal your pre-assigned access code.
4. Enter your pre-assigned access code exactly as it appears below.
5. Complete the online registration form to create your own personal user Login Name and Password.
6. Once your personal Login Name and Password are confirmed by email, go back to www.physioex.com, type in your new Login Name and Password, and click "Log In."

Your Access Code is:

If there is no silver foil covering the access code above, the code may no longer be valid. In that case, you need to either:
- Purchase a new student access kit at your campus bookstore.
- Purchase access online using a major credit card. Go to www.physioex.com and click **Buy Now**.

Important: Please read the License Agreement, located on the launch screen, before using PhysioEx. By using the website, you indicate that you have read, understood, and accepted the terms of this agreement.

PhysioEx™ 6.0 for A&P
Laboratory Simulations in Physiology

PETER ZAO
North Idaho College

TIMOTHY STABLER
Indiana University Northwest

LORI SMITH
American River College

GRETA PETERSON
Middlesex Community College

MARCIA C. GIBSON
University of Wisconsin—Madison
(Histology Review Supplement)

NINA ZANETTI
Siena College

PEARSON
Benjamin Cummings

San Francisco Boston New York
Cape Town Hong Kong London Madrid Mexico City
Montreal Munich Paris Singapore Sidney Tokyo Toronto

Publisher: Daryl Fox

Managing Editor: Wendy Earl

Production Supervisor: David Novak

Media Developers: Cadre Design

Assistant Editor: Ryan Shaw

Benjamin Cummings gratefully acknowledges Carolina
Biological Supply for the use of numerous histology
images found on the PhysioEx CD-ROM.

PhysioEx™ 6.0 Products

For the Anatomy & Physiology Course

PhysioEx™ 6.0 for A&P: Laboratory Simulations in
Physiology
order ISBN 0-8053-8060-4

Instructor's Guide for PhysioEx™ 6.0 for A&P
order ISBN 0-8053-8065-5

For the Human Physiology Course

PhysioEx™ 6.0 for Human Physiology: Laboratory
Simulations in Physiology
order ISBN 0-8053-8061-2

Instructor's Guide for PhysioEx™ 6.0 for Human Physiology
order ISBN 0-8053-8069-8

To locate the Benjamin Cummings sales representative
nearest you, visit **http://www.aw.com/replocator**

ISBN 0-8053-8064-7

1 2 3 4 5 6 7 8 9 10—MAL—09 08 07 06 05

www.aw-bc.com

CONTENTS

Preface iv

Exercise 1 Cell Transport Mechanisms and Permeability 1

Exercise 2 Skeletal Muscle Physiology 12

Exercise 3 Neurophysiology of Nerve Impulses 23

Exercise 4 Endocrine System Physiology 32

Exercise 5 Cardiovascular Dynamics 43

Exercise 6 Frog Cardiovascular Physiology 54

Exercise 7 Respiratory System Mechanics 61

Exercise 8 Chemical and Physical Processes of Digestion 69

Exercise 9 Renal System Physiology 80

Exercise 10 Acid/Base Balance 88

Exercise 11 Blood Analysis 98

Exercise 12 Serological Testing 110

Exercise H Histology Tutorial 121

Histology Review Supplement 123

Review Sheet for Exercise 1 133

Review Sheet for Exercise 2 137

Review Sheet for Exercise 3 141

Review Sheet for Exercise 4 145

Review Sheet for Exercise 5 149

Review Sheet for Exercise 6 153

Review Sheet for Exercise 7 155

Review Sheet for Exercise 8 159

Review Sheet for Exercise 9 163

Review Sheet for Exercise 10 167

Review Sheet for Exercise 11 169

Review Sheet for Exercise 12 173

PREFACE

PhysioEx™ version 6.0 consists of thirteen modules containing 40 physiology lab simulations that may be used to supplement or replace wet labs. This easy-to-use software allows you to repeat labs as often as you like, perform experiments without harming live animals, and conduct experiments that may be difficult to perform in a wet lab environment due to time, cost, or safety concerns. You also have the flexibility to change the parameters of an experiment and observe how outcomes are affected. In addition, PhysioEx includes an extensive histology tutorial that allows you to study histology images at various magnifications. This manual will walk you through each lab step-by-step. You will also find Review Sheets in the back of your manual to test your understanding of the key concepts in each lab.

New to Version 6.0

Note to instructors: If you have used previous versions of PhysioEx, here is a summary of what you will find new to version 6.0:

• *A new module on serological testing* has been added to version 6.0. Four new simulations are included, covering the following topics: direct fluorescent antibody testing for chlamydial infection, Ouchterlony double diffusion, indirect enzyme-linked immunosorbent assay (ELISA) testing for HIV, and Western blot confirmatory testing for HIV.

• The two previous Histology sections have been combined and redesigned, creating *a more powerful Histology Tutorial section*. Students now have the option to search for slides alphabetically, by tissue type, or by organ system. Thirty new images have been added, along with over one hundred new slide descriptions. Students can complete the Histology Review worksheets or simply explore the different types of tissues using this one-stop library of quality histology resources.

• Every copy of PhysioEx 6.0 now includes a CD-ROM version of the PhysioEx 6.0 software program as well as access to the PhysioEx website.

An Instructor's Guide is also available and is free with adoption of this lab manual. Contact your local Benjamin Cummings sales representative for more information. To locate the sales representative for your school, go to http://www.aw.com/replocator.

Topics in This Edition

Exercise 1 Cell Transport Mechanisms and Permeability. Explores how substances cross the cell's membrane. Simple and facilitated diffusion, osmosis, filtration, and active transport are covered.

Exercise 2 Skeletal Muscle Physiology. Provides insights into the complex physiology of skeletal muscle. Electrical stimulation, isometric contractions, and isotonic contractions are investigated.

Exercise 3 Neurophysiology of Nerve Impulses. Investigates stimuli that elicit action potentials, stimuli that inhibit action potentials, and factors affecting nerve conduction velocity.

Exercise 4 Endocrine System Physiology. Investigates the relationship between hormones and metabolism; the effect of estrogen replacement therapy; and the effects of insulin on diabetes.

Exercise 5 Cardiovascular Dynamics. Topics of inquiry include vessel resistance and pump (heart) mechanics.

Exercise 6 Frog Cardiovascular Physiology. Variables influencing heart activity are examined. Topics include setting up and recording baseline heart activity, the refractory period for cardiac muscle, and an investigation of physical and chemical factors that affect enzyme activity.

Exercise 7 Respiratory System Mechanics. Investigates physical and chemical aspects of pulmonary function. Students collect data simulating normal lung volumes. Other activities examine factors such as airway resistance and the effect of surfactant on lung function.

Exercise 8 Chemical and Physical Processes of Digestion. Turns the student's computer into a virtual chemistry lab where enzymes, reagents, and incubation conditions can be manipulated (in compressed time) to examine factors that affect enzyme activity.

Exercise 9 Renal System Physiology. Simulates the function of a single nephron. Topics include factors influencing glomerular filtration, the effect of hormones on urine function, and glucose transport maximum.

Exercise 10   Acid/Base Balance. Topics include respiratory and metabolic acidosis/alkalosis, as well as renal and respiratory compensation.

Exercise 11   Blood Analysis. Covers hematocrit determination, erythrocyte sedimentation rate determination, hemoglobin determination, blood typing, and total cholesterol determination.

Exercise 12   Serological Testing. Investigates antigen-antibody reactions and their role in clinical tests used to diagnose a disease or infection.

Histology Tutorial   Includes over 200 histology images, viewable at various magnifications, organized alphabetically, by body system, and by tissue type, with accompanying descriptions and labels.

Getting Started

To use PhysioEx™ version 6.0, your computer should meet the following minimum requirements (regardless of whether you are using the CD or accessing PhysioEx via the Web):

- **Windows PC:**
  Windows 98 or higher
  266 MHz Intel Pentium processor or greater
  Browser: Internet Explorer 5.0 or higher; Netscape 7.0 or higher*

- **Macintosh (Mac):**
  OS 9.2.2, 10.2.6, 10.2.8, 10.3.5, 10.3.6, 10.3.7
  266 MHz Minimum CPU
  Browser: OS 9: Internet Explorer 5.1.7 or higher; OS X (10): Safari 1.x, Netscape 7.2 or higher, Internet Explorer 5.2.3 or higher

- **Plug-Ins:** Flash Player 7[†], Acrobat Reader 7

- 64MB minimum RAM

- 1024 × 768 screen resolution, millions of colors

- Internet connection: 56K modem minimum for website

* Note: Use of Netscape 6.0 and 6.1 are not recommended due to a known compatibility issue between Netscape 6.0 and 6.1 and the Flash plug-in.

* CD version users: Although you do not need a live Internet connection to run the CD, you do need to have a browser installed on your computer. If you do not have a browser, the CD includes a free copy of Netscape which you may install. See instructions on the CD-liner notes.

[†] CD version users: If you do not have Flash 7 installed on your computer, the CD includes a free Flash installer. See instructions on the CD-liner notes.

Instructions for Getting Started—Mac Users (CD Version)

1.   Put the CD in the CD-ROM drive. Double click the PhysioEx CD icon that appears on your desktop, then double click Start_PhysioEx_6.0 (Mac OSX) or Start_PhysioEx_6.0.app (Mac OS 9.2.2).

2.   Although you do not need a live Internet connection to run PhysioEx, you do need to have a browser (such as Netscape or Internet Explorer) installed on your computer. If you already have a browser installed, proceed to step 3. If you do not have a browser installed, follow the instructions for installing Netscape found on the liner notes that are packaged with your CD.

3.   If you can see a clock onscreen with the clock hands moving, click **Proceed.** If you cannot see the clock, or if you can see the clock but the hands are not moving, follow the instructions for installing Flash 7 found on the liner notes that are packaged with your CD.

4.   On the License Agreement screen, click **Agree** to proceed.

5.   On the screen with the PhysioEx icon at the top, click the License Agreement link to read the full agreement. Then close the License Agreement window and click the Main Menu link.

6.   From the Main Menu, click on the lab you wish to enter.

Instructions for Getting Started—IBM/PC Users (CD Version)

1.   Put the PhysioEx CD in the CD-ROM drive. The program should launch automatically. If autorun is disabled on your machine, double click the My Computer icon on your Windows desktop, double click the PhysioEx icon, and then double click Start_PhysioEx6.0.exe.

2.   Although you do not need a live Internet connection to run PhysioEx, you do need to have a browser (such as Netscape or Internet Explorer) installed on your computer. If you already have a browser installed, proceed to step 3. If you do not have a browser installed, follow the instructions for installing Netscape found on the liner notes that are packaged with your CD.

3.   If you can see a clock onscreen with the clock hands moving, click **Proceed.** If you cannot see the clock, or if you can see the clock but the hands are not moving, follow the instructions for installing Flash 7 found on the liner notes that are packaged with your CD.

4.   On the License Agreement screen, click **Agree** to proceed.

5.   On the screen with the PhysioEx icon at the top, click the License Agreement link to read the full agreement. Then close the License Agreement window, and click the Main Menu link.

6.   From the Main Menu, click on the lab you wish to enter.

Instructions for Getting Started— Web Users

If you have the web version of this manual, follow the instructions for accessing www.physioex.com that appear at the very front of your lab manual.

Technical Support

Visit http://247.aw.com
Email technical support is available 24/7
1-800-677-6337 (8AM-8PM Eastern, Monday-Friday; 5PM-12 midnight Eastern, Sunday)

Cell Transport Mechanisms and Permeability

The molecular composition of the plasma membrane allows it to be selective about what passes through it. It allows nutrients to enter the cell but keeps out undesirable substances. By the same token, valuable cell proteins and other substances are kept within the cell, and excreta or wastes pass to the exterior. This property is known as **differential,** or **selective, permeability.** Transport through the plasma membrane occurs in two basic ways. In **active processes,** the cell provides energy (ATP) to power the transport. In the other, **passive processes,** the transport process is driven by concentration or pressure differences between the interior and exterior of the cell.

Passive Processes

The two key passive processes of membrane transport are diffusion and filtration. Diffusion is an important transport process for every cell in the body. By contrast, filtration usually occurs only across capillary walls. Each of these will be considered in turn.

Diffusion

Recall that all molecules possess *kinetic energy* and are in constant motion. As molecules move about randomly at high speeds, they collide and ricochet off one another, changing direction with each collision. For a given temperature, all matter has about the same average kinetic energy. Because kinetic energy is directly related to both mass and velocity ($KE = \frac{1}{2}\,mv^2$), smaller molecules tend to move faster.

When a **concentration gradient** (difference in concentration) exists, the net effect of this random molecular movement is that the molecules eventually become evenly distributed throughout the environment—in other words, the process called diffusion occurs. Hence, **diffusion** is the movement of molecules from a region of their higher concentration to a region of their lower concentration. Diffusion's driving force is the kinetic energy of the molecules themselves.

The diffusion of particles into and out of cells is modified by the plasma membrane, which constitutes a physical barrier. In general, molecules diffuse passively through the plasma membrane if they are small enough to pass through its pores (and are aided by an electrical gradient), or if they can dissolve in the lipid portion of the membrane as in the case of CO_2 and O_2. The diffusion of solute particles dissolved in water through a differentially permeable membrane is called **simple diffusion.** The diffusion of water through a differentially permeable membrane is called **osmosis.** Both simple diffusion and osmosis involve movement of a substance from an area of its higher concentration to one of its lower concentration, that is, down its concentration gradient.

Objectives

1. To define the following terms: *differential permeability, diffusion (simple diffusion, facilitated diffusion,* and *osmosis), passive* and *active processes* of transport, *bulk-phase endocytosis, phagocytosis,* and *solute pump.*
2. To describe the processes that account for the movement of substances across the plasma membrane, and to indicate the driving force for each.
3. To determine which way substances will move passively through a differentially permeable membrane (given the appropriate information on concentration differences).

Solute Transport Through Nonliving Membranes

This computerized simulation provides information on the passage of water and solutes through semipermeable membranes, which may be applied to the study of transport mechanisms in living membrane-bound cells.

Activity 1:
Simulating Dialysis (Simple Diffusion)

Choose **Cell Transport Mechanisms and Permeability** from the main menu. The opening screen will appear in a few seconds (Figure 1.1). The primary features on the screen when the program starts are a pair of glass beakers perched atop a solutions dispenser, a dialysis membranes cabinet at the right side of the screen, and a data collection unit at the bottom of the display.

The beakers are joined by a membrane holder, which can be equipped with any of the dialysis membranes from the cabinet. Each membrane is represented by a thin colored line suspended in a gray supporting frame. The solute concentration of dispensed solutions is displayed at the side of each beaker. As you work through the experiments, keep in mind that membranes are three-dimensional; thus what appears as a slender line is actually the edge of a membrane sheet.

The solutions you can dispense are listed beneath each beaker. You can choose more than one solution, and the amount to be dispensed is controlled by clicking (+) to increase concentration or (−) to decrease concentration. The chosen solutions are then delivered to their beaker by clicking

Figure 1.1   Opening screen of the Simple Diffusion experiment.

the **Dispense** button on the same side. Clicking the **Start** button opens the membrane holder and begins the experiment. The **Start** button will become a **Pause** button after it is clicked once. To clean the beakers and prepare them for the next run, click **Flush.** Clicking **Pause** and then **Flush** during a run stops the experiment and prepares the beakers for another run. You can adjust the timer for any interval between 5 and 300 minutes; the elapsed time is shown in the small window to the right of the timer.

To move dialysis membranes from the cabinet to the membrane holder, click and hold the mouse on the selected membrane, drag it into position between the beakers, and then release the mouse button to drop it into place. Each membrane possesses a different molecular weight cutoff (MWCO), indicated by the number below it. You can think of MWCO in terms of pore size; the larger the MWCO number, the larger the pores in the membrane.

The **Run Number** window in the data collection unit at the bottom of the screen displays each experimental trial (run). When you click the **Record Data** button, your data is recorded in the computer's memory and is displayed in the data grid at the bottom of the screen. Data displayed in the data grid include the solute (Solute) and membrane (MWCO)

used in a run, the starting concentrations in the left and right beakers (Start Conc. L. and Start Conc. R.), and the average diffusion rate (Avg. Dif. Rate). If you are not satisfied with a run, you can click **Delete Run. Note:** Remember Sodium chloride (NaCl) does not move as a molecule. It dissociates to Na^+ and Cl^- ions in water.

1. Click and hold the mouse on the 20 MWCO membrane, and drag it to the membrane holder between the beakers. Release the mouse button to lock the membrane into place.

2. Now increase the NaCl concentration to be dispensed by clicking the (+) button under the left beaker until the display window reads 9.00 mM. Click **Dispense** to fill the left beaker with 9.00 mM NaCl solution.

3. Click the **Deionized Water** button under the right beaker and then click **Dispense** to fill the right beaker with deionized water.

4. Adjust the timer to 60 minutes (compressed time), then click the **Start** button. When Start is clicked, the barrier between the beakers descends, allowing the solutions in each beaker to have access to the dialysis membrane separating them. Recall that the Start button becomes a Pause button that

Chart 1	Dialysis Results			
	Membrane (MWCO)			
Solute	20	50	100	200
NaCl				
Urea				
Albumin				
Glucose				

allows you to momentarily halt the progress of the experiment so you can see instantaneous diffusion or transport rates.

5. Watch the concentration windows at the side of each beaker for any activity. A level above zero in NaCl concentration in the right beaker indicates that Na^+ and Cl^- ions are diffusing from the left into the right beaker through the semipermeable dialysis membrane. Record your results (+ for diffusion, − for no diffusion) in Chart 1. Click the **Record Data** button to keep your data in the computer's memory.

6. Click the 20 MWCO membrane (in the membrane holder) again to automatically return it to the membranes cabinet and then click **Flush** beneath each beaker to prepare for the next run.

7. Drag the next membrane (50 MWCO) to the holder and repeat steps 2 through 6. Continue the runs until you have tested all four membranes. (Remember: Click **Flush** beneath each beaker between runs.)

8. Now repeat the same experiment three times for urea, albumin, and glucose, respectively. In step 2 you will be dispensing first urea, then albumin, and finally glucose, instead of NaCl.

9. Click **Tools → Print Data** to print your data.

Which solute(s) were able to diffuse into the right beaker from the left?

_____

Which solute(s) did not diffuse?

_____

If the solution in the left beaker contained both urea and albumin, which membrane(s) could you choose to selectively remove the urea from the solution in the left beaker? How would you carry out this experiment?

_____

_____

Assume that the solution in the left beaker contained NaCl in addition to the urea and albumin. How could you set up an experiment so that you removed the urea, but left the NaCl concentration unchanged?

_____

_____

_____ ∎

Facilitated Diffusion

Some molecules are lipid insoluble or too large to pass through plasma membrane pores; instead, they pass through the membrane by a passive transport process called **facilitated diffusion.** In this form of transport, solutes combine with carrier protein molecules in the membrane and are then transported *along* or *down* their concentration gradient. Because facilitated diffusion relies on carrier proteins, solute transport varies with the number of available membrane transport proteins.

Activity 2:
Simulating Facilitated Diffusion

Click the **Experiment** menu and then choose **Facilitated Diffusion.** The opening screen will appear in a few seconds (Figure 1.2). The basic screen layout is similar to that of the previous experiment with only a few modifications to the equipment. You will notice that only NaCl and glucose solutes are available in this experiment, and you will see a Membrane Builder on the right side of the screen.

The (+) and (−) buttons underneath each beaker adjust solute concentration in the solutions to be delivered into each beaker. Similarly, the buttons in the Membrane Builder allow you to control the number of carrier proteins implanted in the membrane when you click the **Build Membrane** button.

In this experiment, you will investigate how glucose transport is affected by the number of available carrier molecules.

1. The Glucose Carriers window in the Membrane Builder should read 500. If not, adjust to 500 by using the (+) or (−) button.

2. Now click **Build Membrane** to insert 500 glucose carrier proteins into the membrane. You should see the membrane appear as a slender line encased in a support structure within the Membrane Builder. Remember that we are looking at the edge of a three-dimensional membrane.

3. Click on the membrane and hold the mouse button down as you drag the membrane to the membrane holder between the beakers. Release the mouse to lock the membrane into place.

4. Adjust the glucose concentration to be delivered to the left beaker to 2.00 mM by clicking the (+) button next to the glucose window until it reads 2.00.

5. To fill the left beaker with the glucose solution, click the **Dispense** button just below the left beaker.

Figure 1.2   Opening screen of the Facilitated Diffusion experiment.

6.   Click the **Deionized Water** button below the right beaker, and then click the **Dispense** button. The right beaker will fill with deionized water.

7.   Set the timer to 60 minutes, and click **Start.** Watch the concentration windows next to the beakers. When the 60 minutes have elapsed, click the **Record Data** button to display glucose transport rate information in the grid at the lower edge of the screen. Record the glucose transport rate in Chart 2.

8.   Click the **Flush** button beneath each beaker to remove any residual solution.

9.   Click the membrane support to return it to the Membrane Builder. Increase the glucose carriers, and repeat steps 2 through 8 using membranes with 700 and then 900 glucose carrier proteins. Record your results in Chart 2 each time.

10.   Repeat steps 1 through 9 at 8.00 m*M* glucose concentration. Record your results in Chart 2.

11.   Click **Tools** → **Print Data** to print your data.

What happened to the rate of facilitated diffusion as the number of protein carriers increased? Explain your answer.

Chart 2	Facilitated Diffusion Results		
Glucose concentration (mM)	No. of glucose carrier proteins		
	500	700	900
2.00			
8.00			

What do you think would happen to the transport rate if you put the same concentration of glucose into both beakers instead of deionized water in the right beaker?

_____

_____

Should NaCl have an effect on glucose diffusion? Explain your answer. Use the simulation to see if it does.

_____

_____

_____ ■

Osmosis

A special form of diffusion, the diffusion of water through a semipermeable membrane, is called **osmosis.** Because water can pass through the pores of most membranes, it can move from one side of a membrane to another relatively unimpeded. Osmosis occurs whenever there is a difference in water concentration on the two sides of a membrane.

If we place distilled water on both sides of a membrane, *net* movement of water will not occur; however, water molecules would still move between the two sides of the membrane. In such a situation, we would say that there is no *net* osmosis. The concentration of water in a solution depends on the number of solutes present. Therefore, increasing the solute concentration coincides with a decrease in water concentration. Because water moves down its concentration gradient, it will always move toward the solution with the highest concentration of solutes. Similarly, solutes also move down their concentration gradient. If we position a *fully* permeable membrane (permeable to solutes and water) between two solutions of differing concentrations, then all substances— solutes and water—will diffuse freely, and an equilibrium will be reached between the two sides of the membrane. However, if we use a semipermeable membrane that is impermeable to the solutes, then we have established a condition where water will move but solutes will not. Consequently, water will move toward the more concentrated solution, resulting in a volume increase. By applying this concept to a closed system where volumes cannot change, we can predict that the pressure in the more concentrated solution would rise.

Activity 3:
Simulating Osmotic Pressure

Click the **Experiment** menu, and then select **Osmosis.** The opening screen will appear in a few seconds (Figure 1.3). The most notable difference in this experiment screen concerns meters atop the beakers that measure pressure changes in the beaker they serve. As before, (+) and (−) buttons control solute concentrations in the dispensed solutions.

1. Drag the 20 MWCO membrane to the holder between the two beakers.

2. Adjust the NaCl concentration to 8.00 mM in the left beaker, and then click the **Dispense** button.

3. Click **Deionized Water** under the right beaker, and then click **Dispense.**

4. Set the timer to 60 minutes, and then click **Start** to run the experiment. Pay attention to the pressure displays. Click the **Record Data** button to retain your data in the computer's memory, and also record the osmotic pressure in Chart 3 below.

5. Click the membrane to return it to the membrane cabinet.

6. Repeat steps 1 through 5 with the 50, 100, and 200 MWCO membranes.

Do you see any evidence of pressure changes in either beaker, using any of the four membranes? If so, which ones?

_____

Does NaCl appear in the right beaker? If so, which membrane(s) allowed it to pass?

_____

_____

7. Now perform the same experiment for albumin and glucose by repeating steps 1 through 6 for each solute. For albumin, dispense 9.00 mM albumin in step 2 (instead of NaCl). For glucose, dispense 10.00 mM glucose in step 2 (instead of NaCl).

8. Click **Tools → Print Data** to print your data.

Answer the following questions using the results you recorded in Chart 3. Use the simulation if you need help formulating a response.

Chart 3	Osmosis Results (pressure in mm Hg)			
Membrane (MWCO)				
Solute	20	50	100	200
Na$^+$Cl$^-$				
Albumin				
Glucose				

Figure 1.3 Opening screen of the Osmosis experiment.

Explain the relationship between solute concentration and osmotic pressure.

_____

_____

Will osmotic pressure be generated if solutes are able to diffuse? Explain your answer.

_____

_____

Because the albumin molecule is much too large to pass through a 100 MWCO membrane, you should have noticed the development of osmotic pressure in the left beaker in the albumin run using the 100 MWCO membrane. What do you think would happen to the osmotic pressure if you replaced

the deionized water in the right beaker with 9.00 mM albumin in that run? (Both beakers would contain 9.00 mM albumin.)

_____

What would happen if you doubled the albumin concentration in the left beaker using any membrane?

_____

In the albumin run using the 200 MWCO membrane, what would happen to the osmotic pressure if you put 10 mM glucose in the right beaker instead of deionized water? Explain your answer.

_____

_____

_____

What if you used the 100 MWCO membrane in the albumin/glucose run described in the previous question?

_____

_____ ■

Activity 4:
Simulating Filtration

Filtration is the process by which water and solutes pass through a membrane (such as a dialysis membrane) from an area of higher hydrostatic (fluid) pressure into an area of lower hydrostatic pressure. Like diffusion, it is a passive process. For example, fluids and solutes filter out of the capillaries in the kidneys into the kidney tubules because blood pressure in the capillaries is greater than the fluid pressure in the tubules. Filtration is not a selective process. The amount of filtrate—fluids and solutes—formed depends almost entirely on the pressure gradient (the difference in pressure on the two sides of the membrane) and on the size of the membrane pores.

Click the **Experiment** menu, and then choose **Filtration.** The opening screen will appear in a few seconds (Figure 1.4). The basic screen elements resemble the other simulations but in a different arrangement. The top beaker can be pressurized to force fluid through the filtration membrane into the bottom beaker. Any of the filtration membranes can be positioned in the holder between the beakers by drag-and-drop as in the previous experiments. The solutions you can dispense are listed to the right of the top beaker and are adjusted by clicking the (+) and (−) buttons. The selected solutions are then delivered to the top beaker by clicking **Dispense.** The top beaker is cleaned and prepared for the next run by clicking **Flush.** You can adjust the timer for any interval between 5 and 300; the elapsed time is shown in the window to the right of the timer. When you click the **Record Data** button, your data is recorded in the computer's memory and is displayed in the data grid at the bottom of the screen.

Solute concentrations in the filtrate are automatically monitored by the *Filtration Rate Analysis unit* to the right of the bottom beaker. After a run you can detect the presence of any solute remaining on a membrane by using the *Membrane Residue Analysis* unit located above the membranes cabinet.

Figure 1.4 Opening screen of the Filtration experiment.

Chart 4	Filtration Results (Filtration Rate, Solute Presence or Absence)			
	Membrane (MWCO)			
Solute	20	50	100	200
NaCl — Rate				
NaCl — Filtrate				
NaCl — Residue				
Urea — Filtrate				
Urea — Residue				
Glucose — Filtrate				
Glucose — Residue				
Powdered charcoal — Filtrate				
Powdered charcoal — Residue				

1. Click and hold the mouse on the 20 MWCO membrane, and drag it to the holder below the top beaker. Release the mouse button to lock the membrane into place.

2. Now adjust the NaCl, urea, glucose, and powdered charcoal windows to 5.00 mg/ml each, and then click **Dispense.**

3. If necessary, adjust the pressure unit atop the beaker until its window reads 50 mm Hg.

4. Set the timer to 60 minutes, and then click **Start.** When the Start button is clicked, the membrane holder below the top beaker retracts, and the solution will flow through the membrane into the beaker below.

5. Watch the Filtration Rate Analysis unit for any activity. A rise in detected solute concentration indicates that the solute particles are moving through the filtration membrane. At the end of the run, record the amount of solute present in the *filtrate* (mg/ml) and the filtration *rate* in Chart 4.

6. Now drag the 20 MWCO membrane to the holder in the Membrane Residue Analysis unit. Click **Start Analysis** to begin analysis (and cleaning) of the membrane. Record your results for solute *residue* presence on the membrane (+ for present, − for not present) in Chart 4, and click the **Record Data** button to keep your data in the computer's memory.

7. Click the 20 MWCO membrane again to automatically return it to the membranes cabinet, and then click **Flush** to prepare for the next run.

8. Repeat steps 1 through 7 three times using 50, 100, and 200 MWCO membranes, respectively.

9. Click **Tools → Print Data** to print your data.

Did the membrane's MWCO affect the filtration rate?

_____

Which solute did not appear in the filtrate using any of the membranes?

_____

What would happen if you increased the driving pressure? Use the simulation to arrive at an answer.

_____

Explain how you can increase the filtration rate through living membranes.

_____

_____

By examining the filtration results, we can predict that the molecular weight of glucose must be

greater than _____ but less than _____. ■

Active Transport

Whenever a cell expends cellular energy (ATP) to move substances across its membrane, the process is referred to as an *active transport process*. Substances moved across cell membranes by active means are generally unable to pass by diffusion. There are several possible reasons why substances may not be able to pass through a membrane by diffusion: they may be too large to pass through the membrane channels, they may not be lipid soluble, or they may have to move against rather than with a concentration gradient.

In one type of active transport, substances move across the membrane by combining with a protein carrier molecule; the process resembles an enzyme-substrate interaction. ATP provides the driving force, and in many cases the substances move against concentration or electrochemical gradients or both. Some of the substances that are moved into the cells by such carriers, commonly called **solute pumps,** are amino acids and some sugars. Both solutes are lipid-insoluble and too large to pass through the membrane channels but are necessary for cell life. On the other hand, sodium ions (Na^+) are ejected from the cells by active transport. There is more Na^+ outside the cell than inside, so the Na^+ tends to remain in the cell unless actively transported out. In the body, the most common type of solute pump is the coupled Na^+-K^+ (sodium-potassium) pump that moves Na^+ and K^+ in opposite directions across cellular membranes. Three Na^+ are ejected for every two K^+ entering the cell.

Engulfment processes such as bulk-phase endocytosis and phagocytosis also require ATP. In **bulk-phase endocytosis,** the cell membrane sinks beneath the material to form a small vesicle, which then pinches off into the cell interior. Bulk-phase endocytosis is most common for taking in liquids containing protein or fat.

In **phagocytosis** (cell eating), parts of the plasma membrane and cytoplasm expand and flow around a relatively large or solid material such as bacteria or cell debris and engulf it, forming a membranous sac called a *phagosome*. The phagosome is then fused with a *lysosome* and its contents are digested. In the human body, phagocytic cells are mainly found among the white blood cells and macrophages that act as scavengers and help protect the body from disease-causing microorganisms and cancer cells.

You will examine various factors influencing the function of solute pumps in the following experiment.

Simulating Active Transport

Click the **Experiment** menu and then choose **Active Transport.** The opening screen will appear in a few seconds (Figure 1.5). This experiment screen resembles the osmosis experiment screen except that an ATP dispenser is substituted for the pressure meters atop the beakers. The (+) and (−) buttons control NaCl, KCl, and glucose concentrations in the dispensed solutions. You will use the Membrane Builder to build membranes containing glucose (facilitated diffusion) carrier proteins and active transport Na^+-K^+ (sodium-potassium) pumps.

In this experiment, we will assume that the left beaker represents the cell's interior and the right beaker represents the extracellular space. The Membrane Builder will insert the Na^+-K^+ (sodium-potassium) pumps into the membrane so Na^+ will be pumped toward the right (out of the cell) while K^+ is simultaneously moved to the left (into the cell).

1. In the Membrane Builder, adjust the number of glucose carriers and the number of sodium-potassium pumps to 500.

2. Click **Build Membrane,** and then drag the membrane to its position in the membrane holder between the beakers.

3. Adjust the NaCl concentration to be delivered to the left beaker to 9.00 m*M*, then click the **Dispense** button.

4. Adjust the KCl concentration to be delivered to the right beaker to 6.00 m*M*, then click **Dispense.**

5. Adjust the ATP dispenser to 1.00 m*M*, then click **Dispense ATP.** This action delivers the chosen ATP concentration to both sides of the membrane.

6. Adjust the timer to 60 min, and then click **Start.** Click **Record Data** after each run.

7. Click **Tools → Print Data** to print your data.

Watch the solute concentration windows at the side of each beaker for any changes in Na^+ and K^+ concentrations. The Na^+ transport rate stops before transport has completed. Why do you think that this happens?

_____

What would happen if you did not dispense any ATP?

_____

Figure 1.5 Opening screen of the Active Transport experiment.

8.   Click either **Flush** button to clean both beakers. Repeat steps 3 through 6, adjusting the ATP concentration to 3.00 m*M* in step 5. Click **Record Data** after each run.

Has the amount of Na^+ transported changed?

_____

What would happen if you decreased the number of sodium-potassium pumps?

_____

Explain how you could show that this phenomenon is not just simple diffusion. (Hint: Adjust the Na^+ concentration in the right beaker.)

_____

_____

9.   Click either **Flush** button to clean both beakers. Now repeat steps 1 through 6 dispensing 9.00 m*M* NaCl into the left beaker and 10.00 m*M* NaCl into the right beaker (instead of 6.00 m*M* KCl). Is Na^+ transport affected by this change? Explain your answer.

_____

_____

What would happen to the rate of ion transport if we increased the number of sodium-potassium pump proteins?

_____

_____

Would Na$^+$ and K$^+$ transport change if we added glucose solution?

_____

_____

10. Click **Tools** → **Print Data** to print your recorded data. ▪

Try adjusting various membrane and solute conditions and attempt to predict the outcome of experimental trials. For example, you could dispense 10 mM glucose into the right beaker instead of deionized water.

2

Skeletal Muscle Physiology

Objectives

1. To define these terms used in describing muscle physiology: *multiple motor unit summation, maximal stimulus, treppe, wave summation,* and *tetanus.*

2. To identify two ways that the mode of stimulation can affect muscle force production.

3. To plot a graph relating stimulus strength and twitch force to illustrate graded muscle response.

4. To explain how slow, smooth, sustained contraction is possible in a skeletal muscle.

5. To graphically understand the relationships between passive, active, and total forces.

6. To identify the conditions under which muscle contraction is isometric or isotonic.

7. To describe in terms of length and force the transitions between isometric and isotonic conditions during a single muscle twitch.

8. To describe the effects of resistance and starting length on the initial velocity of shortening.

9. To explain why muscle force remains constant during isotonic shortening.

10. To explain experimental results in terms of muscle structure.

Skeletal muscles are composed of hundreds to thousands of individual cells, each doing their share of work in the production of force. As their name suggests, skeletal muscles move the skeleton. Skeletal muscles are remarkable machines; while allowing us the manual dexterity to create magnificent works of art, they are also capable of generating the brute force needed to lift a 100-lb. sack of concrete. When a skeletal muscle from an experimental animal is electrically stimulated, it behaves in the same way as a stimulated muscle in the intact body, that is, in vivo. Hence, such an experiment gives us valuable insight into muscle behavior.

This set of computer simulations demonstrates many important physiological concepts of skeletal muscle contraction. The program graphically provides all the equipment and materials necessary for you, the investigator, to set up experimental conditions and observe the results. In student-conducted laboratory investigations, there are many ways to approach a problem, and the same is true of these simulations. The instructions will guide you in your investigation, but you should also try out alternate approaches to gain insight into the logical methods used in scientific experimentation.

Try this approach: As you work through the simulations for the first time, follow the instructions closely and answer the questions posed as you go. Then try asking "What if . . . ?" questions to test the validity of your hypotheses. The major advantages of these computer simulations are that the muscle cannot be accidentally damaged, lab equipment will not break down at the worst possible time, and you will have ample time to think critically about the processes being investigated.

Because you will be working with a simulated muscle and oscilloscope display, you need to watch both carefully during the experiments. Think about what is happening in each situation. You need to understand how you are experimentally manipulating the muscle in order to understand your results.

Electrical Stimulation

A contracting skeletal muscle will produce force and/or shortening when nervous or electrical stimulation is applied. The graded contractile response of a whole muscle reflects the number of motor units firing at a given time. Strong muscle contraction implies that many motor units are activated and each unit has maximally contracted. Weak contraction means that few motor units are active; however, the activated units are maximally contracted. By increasing the number of motor units firing, we can produce a steady increase in muscle force, a process called **recruitment** or **motor unit summation.**

Regardless of the number of motor units activated, a single contraction of skeletal muscle is called a muscle twitch. A tracing of a muscle twitch is divided into three phases: latent, contraction, and relaxation. The latent phase is a short period between the time of stimulation and the beginning of contraction. Although no force is generated during this interval, chemical changes occur intracellularly in preparation for contraction. During contraction, the myofilaments are sliding past each other, and the muscle shortens. Relaxation takes place when contraction has ended and the muscle returns to its normal resting state and length.

The first activity you will conduct simulates an **isometric,** or **fixed length, contraction** of an isolated skeletal muscle. This activity allows you to investigate how the strength and frequency of an electrical stimulus affect whole muscle function. Note that these simulations involve indirect stimulation by an electrode placed on the surface of the muscle. This differs from the situation in vivo where each fiber in the muscle receives direct stimulation via a nerve ending. In other words, increasing the intensity of the electrical stimulation mimics how the nervous system increases the number of motor units activated.

Single Stimulus

Choose **Skeletal Muscle Physiology** from the main menu. The opening screen will appear in a few seconds (Figure 2.1). The oscilloscope display, the grid at the top of the screen, is the most important part of the screen because it

Figure 2.1   Opening screen of the Single Stimulus experiment.

graphically displays the contraction data for analysis. Time is displayed on the horizontal axis. A full sweep is initially set at 200 msec. However, you can adjust the sweep time from 200 msec to 1000 msec by clicking and dragging the **200** msec button at the lower right corner of the oscilloscope display to the left to a new position on the time axis. The force (in grams) produced by muscle contraction is displayed on the vertical axis. Clicking the **Clear Tracings** button at the bottom right of the oscilloscope erases all muscle twitch tracings from the oscilloscope display.

The *electrical stimulator* is the equipment seen just beneath the oscilloscope display. Clicking **Stimulate** delivers the electrical shock to the muscle through the electrodes lying on the surface of the muscle. Stimulus voltage is set by clicking the (+) or (−) buttons next to the voltage window. Three small windows to the right of the Stimulate button display the force measurements. *Active force* is produced during muscle contraction, while *passive force* results from the muscle being stretched (much like a rubber band). The *total force* is the sum of active and passive forces. The red arrow at the left of the oscilloscope display is an indicator of passive force. After the muscle is stimulated, the **Measure** button at the right edge of the electrical stimulator becomes active. When the Measure button is clicked, a vertical orange line will be displayed at the left edge of the oscilloscope display. Clicking the arrow buttons below the Measure button moves the orange line horizontally across the screen. The Time window displays the difference in time between the zero point on the X-axis and the intersection between the orange measure line and the muscle twitch tracing.

The muscle is suspended in the support stand to the left of the oscilloscope display. The hook through the upper tendon of the muscle is part of the force transducer, which measures the force produced by the muscle. The hook through the lower tendon secures the muscle in place. The weight cabinet just below the muscle support stand is not active in this experiment; it contains weights you will use in the isotonic contraction part of the simulation. You can adjust the starting length of the muscle by clicking the (+) or (−) buttons located next to the Muscle Length display window.

When you click the **Record Data** button in the data collection unit below the electrical stimulator, your data is recorded in the computer's memory and is displayed in the data grid at the bottom of the screen. Data displayed in the data grid include the voltage, muscle length, and active, passive, and total force measurements. If you are not satisfied with a single run, you can click **Delete Line** to erase a single line of data. Clicking the **Clear Table** button will remove all accumulated data in the experiment and allow you to start over.

Activity 1:
Practicing Generating a Tracing

1.   Click the **Stimulate** button once. Because the beginning voltage is set to zero, no muscle activity should result. You will see a blue line moving across the bottom of the oscilloscope display. This blue line will indicate muscle force in the experiments. If the tracings move too slowly across the screen, click and hold the **200** button at the lower right

corner of the oscilloscope and drag it to the left to the 40 msec mark and release it. This action resets the total sweep time to 1000 msec to speed up the display time.

2.   Click and hold the (+) button beneath the Stimulate button until the voltage window reads 3.0 volts. Click **Stimulate** once. You will see the muscle react, and a contraction tracing will appear on the screen. Notice that the muscle tracing color alternates between blue and yellow each time the Stimulate button is clicked to enhance the visual difference between twitch tracings. You can click the **Clear Tracings** button as needed to clean up the oscilloscope display. To retain your data, click the **Record Data** button at the end of each stimulus.

3.   Change the voltage to 5.0 volts, and click **Stimulate** again. Notice how the force of contraction also changes. Identify the latent, contraction, and relaxation phases in the tracings.

4.   You may print your data by clicking **Tools → Print Data.** You may also print out hard copies of the graphs you generate by clicking on **Tools → Print Graph.**

Feel free to experiment with anything that comes to mind to get a sense of how whole muscle responds to an electrical stimulus. ∎

Activity 2:
Determining the Latent Period

1.   Click **Clear Tracings** to erase the oscilloscope display. The voltage should be set to 5.0 volts.

2.   Drag the **200** msec button to the right edge of the oscilloscope.

3.   Click the **Stimulate** button once, and allow the tracing to complete.

4.   When you measure the length of the latent period from a printed graph, you measure the time between the application of the stimulus and the beginning of the first observable response (increase in force). The computer can't "look ahead," anticipating the change in active force. To measure the length of the latent period using the computer, click the **Measure** button. Then click the right arrow button next to the **Time** window repeatedly until you notice the first increase in the Active Force window. This takes you beyond the actual length of the latent period. Now click the left arrow button next to the **Time** window until the Active Force window again reads zero. At this point the computer is measuring the time between the application of the stimulus and the last point where the active force is zero (just prior to contraction).

How long is the latent period? _____ msec

What occurs in the muscle during this apparent lack of activity?

_____

_____ ∎

The Graded Muscle Response to Increased Stimulus Intensity

As the stimulus to a muscle is increased, the amount of force produced by the muscle also increases. As more voltage is delivered to the whole muscle, more muscle fibers are activated and the total force produced by the muscle is increased. Maximal contraction occurs when all the muscle cells have been activated. Any stimulation beyond this voltage will not increase the force of contraction. This experiment mimics muscle activity in vivo where the recruitment of additional motor units increases the total force produced. This phenomenon is called *multiple motor unit summation*.

Activity 3:
Investigating Graded Muscle Response to Increased Stimulus Intensity

1. Click **Clear Tracings** if there are tracings on your screen.

2. Set the voltage to 0.0, and click **Stimulate.**

3. Click **Record Data.** If you decide to redo a single stimulus, choose the data line in the grid and click **Delete Line** to erase that single line of data. If you want to repeat the entire experiment, click the **Clear Table** button to erase all data recorded to that point.

4. Repeat steps 2 and 3, increasing the voltage by 0.5 each time until you reach the maximum voltage of 10.0. Be sure to select **Record Data** each time.

5. Observe the twitch tracings. Click on the **Tools** menu and then choose **Plot Data.**

6. Use the slider bars to display Active Force on the Y-axis and Voltage on the X-axis.

7. Use your graph to answer the following questions:

What is the minimal, or threshold, stimulus? _____ V

What is the maximal stimulus? _____ V

How can you explain the increase in force that you observe?

_____

_____

What type of summation is this? _____

_____

8. Click **Print Plot** at the top left corner of the Plot Data window to print a hard copy of the graph. When finished, click the X at the top right of the plot window.

9. Click **Tools → Print Data** to print your data. ■

Multiple Stimulus

Choose **Multiple Stimulus** from the **Experiment** menu. The opening screen will appear in a few seconds (Figure 2.2).

The only significant change to the onscreen equipment is found in the electrical stimulator. The measuring equipment has been removed and other controls have been added: The **Multiple Stimulus** button is a toggle that allows you to alternately start and stop the electrical stimulator. When Multiple Stimulus is first clicked, its name changes to Stop Stimulus, and electrical stimuli are delivered to the muscle at the rate specified in the Stimuli/sec window until the muscle completely fatigues or the stimulator is turned off. The stimulator is turned off by clicking the **Stop Stimulus** button. The stimulus rate is adjusted by clicking the (+) or (−) buttons next to the Stimuli/sec window.

Activity 4:
Investigating Treppe

When a muscle first contracts, the force it is able to produce is less than the force it is able to produce in subsequent contractions within a relatively narrow time span. A myogram, a recording of a muscle twitch, reveals this phenomenon as the **treppe,** or staircase, effect. For the first few twitches, each successive stimulation produces slightly more force than the previous contraction as long as the muscle is allowed to fully relax between stimuli, and the stimuli are delivered relatively close together. Treppe is thought to be caused by increased efficiency of the enzyme systems within the cell and increased availability of intracellular calcium.

1. The voltage should be set to 8.2 volts, and the muscle length should be 75 mm.

2. Drag the **200 msec** button to the center of the X-axis time range.

3. Be sure that you fully understand the following three steps before you proceed.

• Click **Single Stimulus.** Watch the twitch tracing carefully.

• After the tracing shows that the muscle has completely relaxed, immediately click **Single Stimulus** again.

• When the second twitch completes, click **Single Stimulus** once more and allow the tracing to complete.

4. Click **Tools → Print Graph.**

What happens to force production with each subsequent stimulus?

_____

_____ ■

Activity 5:
Investigating Wave Summation

As demonstrated in Activity 3 with single stimuli, multiple motor unit summation is one way to increase the amount of

Figure 2.2 Opening screen of the Multiple Stimulus experiment.

force produced by muscle. Multiple motor unit summation relied on increased stimulus *intensity* in that simulation. Another way to increase force is by wave, or temporal, summation. **Wave summation** is achieved by increasing the stimulus *frequency,* or rate of stimulus delivery to the muscle. Wave summation occurs because the muscle is already in a partially contracted state when subsequent stimuli are delivered.

Tetanus can be considered an extreme form of wave summation that results in a steady, sustained contraction. In effect, the muscle does not have any chance to relax because it is being stimulated at such a high frequency. This fuses the force peaks so that we observe a smooth tracing.

1. Click **Clear Tracings** to erase the oscilloscope display.

2. Set and keep the voltage at the maximal stimulus (8.2 volts) and the muscle length at 75 mm.

3. Drag the **200** msec button to the right edge of the oscilloscope display unless you are using a slower computer.

4. Click **Single Stimulus,** and then click **Single Stimulus** again when the muscle has relaxed about halfway.

You may click **Tools → Print Graph** any time you want to print graphs generated during this activity.

Is the peak force produced in the second contraction greater

than that produced by the first stimulus? _____

5. Try stimulating again at greater frequencies by clicking the **Single Stimulus** button several times in rapid succession.

Is the total force production even greater? _____

6. To see if you can produce smooth, sustained contraction at Active Force = 2 gms, try rapidly clicking **Single Stimulus** several times.

Is it possible to produce a smooth contraction (fused force peaks), or does the force rise and fall periodically?

_____

7.   Using the same method as in step 6, try to produce a smooth contraction at 3 gms.

Is the trace smoother (less height between peaks and valleys)

this time? _____

Because there is a limit to how fast you can manually click the Single Stimulus button, what do you think would happen to the smoothness of the tracing if you could click even faster?

_____

_____

_____

8.   So far you have been using the maximal stimulus. What do you think would happen if you used a lower voltage?

_____

_____

_____

9.   Use the concepts of motor unit summation and stimulus frequency to explain how human skeletal muscles work to achieve smooth, steady contractions at all desired levels of force.

_____

_____

_____

_____ ▪

Activity 6:
Investigating Fusion Frequency

1.   Click **Clear Tracings** to erase the oscilloscope display.

2.   The voltage should be set to 8.2 volts, and the muscle length should be 75 mm.

3.   Adjust the stimulus rate to 30 stimuli/sec.

4.   The following steps constitute a single "run." Become familiar with the procedure for completing a run before continuing.

•   Click **Multiple Stimulus.**

•   When the tracing is close to the right side of the screen, click **Stop Stimulus** to turn off the stimulator.

•   Click **Record Data** to retain your data in the grid in the bottom of the screen and in the computer's memory. Click **Tools → Print Graph** to print a hard copy of your graph at any point during this activity.

   If you decide to redo a single run, choose the data line in the grid and click **Delete Line** to erase that single line of data. If you want to repeat the entire experiment, click the **Clear Table** button to erase all data recorded thus far.

Describe the appearance of the tracing.

_____

_____

5.   Repeat step 4, increasing the stimulation rate by 10 stimuli/sec each time up to 150 stimuli/sec.

How do the tracings change as the stimulus rate is increased?

_____

_____

6.   When you have finished observing the twitch tracings, click the **Tools** menu, and then choose **Plot Data.**

7.   Set the Y-axis slider to display Active Force and the X-axis slider to display Stimuli/sec.

From your graph, estimate the stimulus rate above which there appears to be no significant increase in force.

_____ stimuli/sec

This rate is the *fusion frequency*, also called tetanus.

8.   Click **Print Plot** at the top left of the Plot Data window. When finished, click the X at the top right of the plot window.

9.   Reset the stimulus rate to the fusion frequency identified in step 7.

10. Try to produce a smooth contraction at Force = 2 gms and Force = 3 gms by adjusting only the stimulus intensity, or voltage, using the following procedure.

•   Decrease the voltage to a starting point of 1.0 volt, and click **Multiple Stimulus.**

•   Click **Stop Stimulus** to turn off the stimulator when the tracing is near the right side of the oscilloscope display.

•   If the force produced is not smooth and continuous at the desired level of force, increase the voltage in 0.1-volt increments and stimulate as above until you achieve a smooth force at 2 gms and again at 3 gms.

What stimulus intensity produced smooth force at Force = 2 gms?

_____ V

Which intensity produced smooth contraction at Force = 3 gms?

_____ V

Explain what must be happening in the muscle to achieve smooth contraction at different force levels.

_____

_____

_____

_____

_____ ■

Activity 7:
Investigating Muscle Fatigue

A prolonged period of sustained contraction will result in **muscle fatigue,** a condition in which the tissue has lost its ability to contract. Fatigue results when a muscle cell's ATP consumption is faster than its production. Consequently, increasingly fewer ATP molecules are available for the contractile parts within the muscle cell.

1. Click **Clear Tracings** to erase the oscilloscope display.

2. The voltage should be set to 8.2 volts, and the muscle length should be 75 mm.

3. Adjust the stimulus rate to 120 stimuli/sec.

4. Click **Multiple Stimulus,** allow the tracing to sweep through three screens, and then click **Stop Stimulus** to stop the stimulator.

Click **Tools → Print Graph** at any time to print graphs during this activity. Click **Tools → Print Data** to print your data.

Why does the force begin to fall with time? Note that a fall in force indicates muscle fatigue.

_____

_____

5. Click **Clear Tracings** to erase the oscilloscope display. Keep the same settings as before.

6. You will be clicking **Multiple Stimulus** on and off three times to demonstrate fatigue with recovery. Read the steps below before proceeding.

• Click **Multiple Stimulus.**

• When the tracing reaches the middle of the screen, briefly turn off the stimulator by clicking **Stop Stimulus,** then immediately click **Multiple Stimulus** again.

• You will see a dip in the force tracing where you turned the stimulator off and then on again. The force tracing will continue to drop as the muscle fatigues.

• Before the muscle fatigues completely, repeat the on/off cycle twice more without clearing the screen.

Turning the stimulator off allows a small measure of recovery. The muscle will produce force for a longer period if the stimulator is briefly turned off than if the stimulations were allowed to continue without interruption. Explain why.

_____

_____

_____

7. To see the difference between continuous multiple stimulation and multiple stimulation with recovery, click **Multiple Stimulus** and let the tracing fall without interruption to zero force. This tracing will follow the original myogram exactly until the first "dip" is encountered, after which you will notice a difference in the amount of force produced between the two runs.

Describe the difference between the current tracing and the myogram generated in step 6.

_____

_____

_____

_____

_____

_____

_____ ■

Isometric Contraction

Isometric contraction is the condition in which muscle length does not change regardless of the amount of force generated by the muscle (_iso_ = same, _metric_ = length). This is accomplished experimentally by keeping both ends of the muscle in a fixed position while stimulating it electrically. Resting length (length of the muscle before contraction) is an important factor in determining the amount of force that a muscle can develop. Passive force is generated by stretching the muscle and is due to the elastic properties of the tissue itself. Active force is generated by the physiological contraction of the muscle. Think of the muscle as having two force properties: it exerts passive force when it is stretched (like a rubber band exerts passive force) and active force when it contracts. Total force is the sum of passive and active forces, and it is what we experimentally measure.

This simulation allows you to set the resting length of the experimental muscle and stimulate it with individual maximal stimulus shocks. A graph relating the forces generated to the length of the muscle will be automatically plotted as you stimulate the muscle. The results of this simulation can then be applied to human muscles in order to understand how

Figure 2.3 Opening screen of the Isometric Contraction experiment.

optimum resting length will result in maximum force production. In order to understand why muscle tissue behaves as it does, it is necessary to comprehend contraction at the cellular level. Hint: If you have difficulty understanding the results of this exercise, review the sliding filament model of muscle contraction. Then think in terms of sarcomeres that are too short, too long, or just the right length.

Choose **Isometric Contraction** from the **Experiment** menu. The opening screen will appear in a few seconds (Figure 2.3). Notice that the oscilloscope is now divided into two parts. The left side of the scope displays the muscle twitch tracing. The active, passive, and total force data points are plotted on the right side of the screen.

Activity 8:
Investigating Isometric Contraction

1.   The voltage should be set to the maximal stimulus (8.2 volts), and the muscle length should be 75 mm.

2.   To see how the equipment works, stimulate once by clicking **Stimulate.** You should see a single muscle twitch tracing on the left oscilloscope display and three data points representing active, passive, and total force on the right display. The yellow box represents the total force and the red dot it contains symbolizes the superimposed active force. The green square represents the passive force data point.

3.   Try adjusting the muscle length by clicking the (+) or (−) buttons located next to the Muscle Length window, and watch the effect on the muscle.

4.   When you feel comfortable with the equipment, click **Clear Tracings** and **Clear Plot.**

5.   Now stimulate at different muscle lengths using the following procedure.

•   Shorten the muscle to a length of 50 mm by clicking the (−) button next to the Muscle Length window.

•   Click **Stimulate** and, when the tracing is complete, click **Record Data.**

•   Repeat the **Stimulate** and **Record Data** sequence, increasing the muscle length by 2 mm each time until you reach the maximum muscle length of 100 mm.

6. Carefully examine the active, passive, and total force plots in the right oscilloscope display.

7. Click **Tools → Print Data** to print your data.

What happens to the passive and active forces as the muscle length is increased from 50 mm to 100 mm?

Passive force:

_____

_____

Active force:

_____

_____

Total force:

_____

_____

Explain the dip in the total force curve. (Hint: Keep in mind you are measuring the sum of active and passive forces.)

_____

_____

_____

_____

_____ ■

Isotonic Contraction

During **isotonic contraction,** muscle length changes, but the force produced stays the same (*iso* = same, *tonic* = force). Unlike the isometric exercise in which both ends of the muscle are held in a fixed position, one end of the muscle remains free in the isotonic contraction exercise. Different weights can then be attached to the free end while the other end is fixed in position on the force transducer. If the weight is not too great, the muscle will be able to lift it with a certain velocity. You can think of lifting an object from the floor as an example: if the object is light it can be lifted quickly (high velocity), whereas a heavier weight will be lifted with a slower velocity. Try to transfer the idea of what is happening in the simulation to the muscles of your arm when you lift a weight. The two important variables in this exercise are starting length of the muscle and resistance (weight) applied. You have already examined the effect of starting length on muscle force production in the previous exercise. Now you will change both muscle length and resistance to investigate how

such changes affect the speed of skeletal muscle shortening. Both variables can be independently altered, and the results are graphically presented on the screen.

Choose **Isotonic Contraction** from the **Experiment** menu. The opening screen will appear in a few seconds (Figure 2.4). The general operation of the equipment is the same as in the previous experiments. In this simulation, the weight cabinet doors are open. You will attach weights to the lower tendon of the muscle by clicking and holding the mouse on any weight in the cabinet and then dragging-and-dropping the weight's hook onto the lower tendon. The Muscle Length window displays the length achieved when the muscle is stretched by hanging a weight from its lower tendon. You can click the (+) and (−) buttons next to the Platform Height window to change the position of the platform on which the weight rests. Click on the weight again to automatically return it to the weight cabinet. The electrical stimulator displays the initial velocity of muscle shortening in the Velocity window to the right of the Voltage control.

Activity 9:
Investigating the Effect of Load on Skeletal Muscle

1. Set the voltage to the maximal stimulus (8.2 volts).

2. Drag-and-drop the 0.5-g weight onto the muscle's lower tendon.

3. Platform height should be 75 mm.

4. Click **Stimulate** and simultaneously watch the muscle action and the oscilloscope tracing.

5. Click the **Record Data** button to retain and display the data in the grid.

What do you see happening to the muscle during the flat part of the tracing? Click **Stimulate** to repeat if you wish to see the muscle action again.

_____

_____

Does the force the muscle produces change during the flat part of the tracing (increase, decrease, or stay the same)?

_____

Describe the muscle activity during the flat part of the tracing in terms of isotonic contraction and relaxation.

_____

_____

_____

_____

Circle the correct terms in parentheses in the following sequence:

The force rises during the first part of the muscle tracing due to (isometric, isotonic) contraction. The fall in force on the right side of the tracing corresponds to (isometric, isotonic) relaxation.

6. Return the 0.5-g weight to the cabinet. Drag the 1.5-g weight to the muscle. Click **Stimulate,** and then click **Record Data.**

Which of the two weights used so far results in the highest initial velocity of shortening?

_____

7. Repeat step 6 for the remaining two weights.
8. Choose **Plot Data** from the **Tools** menu.

9. Set Weight as the X-axis and Total Force as the Y-axis by dragging the slider bars. Click **Print Plot** if you wish to print the graph.

What does the plot reveal about the resistance and the initial velocity of shortening?

_____

_____

_____

10. Close the plot window. If you wish, click **Tools → Print Data** to print your data.

11. Click **Clear Table** in the data control unit at the bottom of the screen. Click **Yes** when you are asked if you want to erase all data in the table.

12. Return the current weight to the weight cabinet.

Figure 2.4   Opening screen of the Isotonic Contraction experiment.

13. Attach the 1.5-g weight to the muscle and run through the range of starting lengths from 60–90 mm in 5-mm increments. Be sure to click **Record Data** after each stimulus.

14. After all runs have been completed, choose **Plot Data** from the **Tools** menu.

15. Set Length as the X-axis and Velocity as the Y-axis by dragging the slider bars. Click **Print Plot** if you wish to print the graph.

Describe the relationship between starting length and initial velocity of shortening.

_____

_____

_____

_____

Do these results support your ideas in the isometric contraction part of this exercise?

_____

16. Close the plot window. If you wish, click **Tools → Print Data.**

Can you set up a contraction that is completely isometric?

_____ One that is completely isotonic? _____

Explain your answers.

_____

_____

_____

_____ ■

Histology Review Supplement

Turn to page 124 for a review of skeletal muscle tissue.

Neurophysiology of Nerve Impulses

The Nerve Impulse

Neurons have two major physiological properties: **irritability,** or the ability to respond to stimuli and convert them into nerve impulses, and **conductivity,** the ability to transmit an impulse (in this case, to take the neural impulse and pass it along the cell membrane). In the resting neuron (i.e., a neuron that does not have any neural impulses), the exterior of the cell membrane is positively charged and the interior of the neuron is negatively charged. This difference in electrical charge across the plasma membrane is referred to as the **resting membrane potential,** and the membrane is said to be **polarized.** The **sodium-potassium pump** in the membrane maintains the difference in electrical charge established by diffusion of ions. This active transport mechanism moves 3 sodium (Na^+) ions out of the cell while moving in 2 potassium (K^+) ions. Therefore, the major cation (positively charged ion) outside the cell in the extracellular fluid is Na^+, while the major cation inside the cell is K^+. The inner surface of the cell membrane is more negative than the outer surface, mainly due to intracellular proteins, which, at body pH, tend to be negatively charged.

The resting membrane potential can be measured with a voltmeter by putting a recording electrode just inside the cell membrane with a reference, or ground, electrode outside the membrane (see Figure 3.1). In the giant squid axon (where most early neural research was conducted), or in the frog axon that will be used in this exercise, the resting membrane potential is measured at −70 millivolts (mV). (In humans, the resting membrane potential typically measures between −40 mV and −90 mV.)

Objectives

1. To define the following terms: *irritability, conductivity, resting membrane potential, polarized, sodium-potassium pump, threshold stimulus, depolarization, action potential, repolarization, hyperpolarization, absolute refractory period, relative refractory period, nerve impulse, compound nerve action potential,* and *conduction velocity.*

2. To list at least four different stimuli capable of generating an action potential.

3. To list at least two agents capable of inhibiting an action potential.

4. To describe the relationship between nerve size and conduction velocity.

5. To describe the relationship between nerve myelination and conduction velocity.

Figure 3.1 Resting membrane potential is measured with a voltmeter.

(a)

(b)

(c)

(d)

Since in the resting cell Na+ ions tend to diffuse into the cell and K+ ions tend to diffuse out of the cell, the resting potential is maintained by the active sodium-potassium pump.

(e)

Changes in the membrane charge during depolarization and repolarization (steps b through d).

(f)

Figure 3.2 **The nerve impulse.** **(a)** Resting membrane potential (−70 mV). There is an excess of positive ions outside the cell, with Na+ the predominant extracellular fluid ion and K+ the predominant intracellular ion. The plasma membrane has a low permeability to Na+. **(b)** Depolarization—reversal of the resting potential. Application of a stimulus changes the membrane permeability, and Na+ are allowed to diffuse rapidly into the cell. **(c)** Generation of the action potential or nerve impulse. If the stimulus is of adequate intensity, the depolarization wave spreads rapidly along the entire length of the membrane. **(d)** Repolarization—reestablishment of the resting potential. The negative charge on the internal plasma membrane surface and the positive charge on its external surface are reestablished by diffusion of K+ out of the cell, proceeding in the same direction as in depolarization. **(e)** The original ionic concentrations of the resting state are restored by the sodium-potassium pump. **(f)** A tracing of an action potential.

When a neuron is activated by a stimulus of adequate intensity, known as a **threshold stimulus,** the membrane at its *trigger zone,* typically the axon hillock, briefly becomes more permeable to Na+ ions (sodium gates in the cell membrane open). Na+ rushes into the cell, increasing the number of positive ions inside the cell and changing the membrane polarity. The interior surface of the membrane becomes less negative and the exterior surface becomes less positive, a phenomenon called **depolarization** (see Figure 3.2a).

When depolarization reaches a certain point called **threshold,** an **action potential** is initiated (see Figure 3.2c) and the polarity of the membrane reverses.

When the membrane depolarizes, the resting membrane potential of −70 mV becomes less negative. When the membrane potential reaches 0 mV, indicating there is no charge difference across the membrane, the sodium ion channels start to close and potassium ion channels open. By the time the sodium ions channels finally close, the membrane potential has reached +35 mV. The opening of the potassium ion channels allows K^+ to flow out of the cell down their electrochemical gradient—remember, like ions are repelled from each other. The flow of K^+ out of the cell causes the membrane potential to move in a negative direction. This is referred to as **repolarization** (see Figure 3.2d). This repolarization occurs within a millisecond of the initial sodium influx and reestablishes the resting membrane potential. Actually, by the time the potassium gates close, the cell membrane has undergone a **hyperpolarization,** slipping to perhaps −75 mV. With the gates closed, the resting membrane potential is quickly returned to the normal resting membrane potential.

When the sodium gates are open, the membrane is totally insensitive to additional stimuli, regardless of the force of stimulus. The cell is in what is called the **absolute refractory period.** During repolarization, the membrane may be stimulated if a very strong stimulus is used. This period is called the **relative refractory period.**

The action potential, once started, is a self-propagating phenomenon, spreading rapidly along the neuron membrane. The action potential follows the *all-or-none response,* in which the neuron membrane either depolarizes 100% or not at all. In neurons, the action potential is also called a **nerve impulse.** When it reaches the axon terminal, it triggers the release of neurotransmitters into the synaptic cleft. Depending on the situation, the neurotransmitter will either excite or inhibit the postsynaptic neuron.

In order to study nerve physiology, we will use a frog nerve and several electronic instruments. The first instrument is the *electronic stimulator.* Nerves can be stimulated by chemicals, touch, or electric shock. The electronic stimulator administers an electric shock that is pure direct current (DC), and allows duration, frequency, and voltage of the shock to be precisely controlled. The stimulator has two output terminals; the positive terminal is red and the negative terminal is black. Voltage leaves the stimulator via the red terminal, passes through the item to be stimulated (in this case, the nerve), and returns to the stimulator at the black terminal to complete the circuit.

The second instrument is the **oscilloscope,** an instrument that measures voltage changes over a period of time. The face of the oscilloscope is similar to a black-and-white television screen. The screen of the oscilloscope is the front of a tube with a filament at the other end. The filament is heated and gives off a beam of electrons that passes to the front of the tube. Electronic circuitry allows the electron beam to be brought across the screen in preset time intervals. When the electrons hit the phosphorescent material on the inside of the screen, a spot on the screen will glow. When we apply a stimulus to a nerve, the oscilloscope screen will display one of the following three results: no response, a flat line, or a graph with a peak. A graph with a peak indicates that an action potential has been generated.

While performing the following experiments, keep in mind that you are working with a nerve, which consists of many neurons—you are not working with just a single neuron. The action potential you will see on the oscilloscope screen reflects the cumulative action potentials of all the neurons in the nerve, called a **compound nerve action potential.** Although an action potential follows the all-or-none law within a single neuron, it does not necessarily follow this law within an entire nerve. When you electrically stimulate a nerve at a given voltage, the stimulus may result in the depolarization of most of the neurons but not necessarily all of them. To achieve depolarization of *all* of the neurons, a higher stimulus voltage may be needed.

Eliciting a Nerve Impulse

In the following experiments, you will be investigating what kinds of stimuli trigger an action potential. To begin, select **Neurophysiology of Nerve Impulses** from the main menu. The opening screen will appear in a few seconds (see Figure 3.3). Note that a sciatic nerve from a frog has been placed into the nerve chamber. Leads go from the stimulator output to the nerve chamber, the vertical box on the left side. Leads also go from the nerve chamber to the oscilloscope. Notice that these leads are red and black. The current travels along the red lead to the nerve. When the nerve depolarizes, it will generate an electrical current that will travel along the red wire to the oscilloscope and back to the nerve along the black wire.

Activity 1:
Electrical Stimulation

1. Set the voltage at 1.0 V by clicking the (+) button next to the **Voltage** display.

2. Click **Single Stimulus.**

Do you see any kind of response on the oscilloscope

screen? _____

If you saw no response, or a flat line indicating no action potential, click the **Clear** button on the oscilloscope, increase the voltage, and click **Single Stimulus** again until you see a trace (deflection of the line) that indicates an action potential.

What was the *threshold voltage,* that is, the voltage at which

you first saw an action potential? _____ V

Click **Record Data** on the data collection box to record your results.

3. If you wish to print your graph, click **Tools** and then **Print Graph.** You may do this each time you generate a graph on the oscilloscope screen.

4. Increase the voltage by 0.5 V, and click **Single Stimulus.**

How does this tracing compare to the one trace that was generated at the threshold voltage? (Hint: Look very carefully at the tracings.)

_____

Figure 3.3 Opening screen of the Eliciting a Nerve Impulse experiment.

What reason can you give for your answer?

_____

_____

_____

Click **Record Data** on the data collection box to record your results.

5. Continue to increase the voltage by 0.5 V and to click **Single Stimulus** until you find the point beyond which no further increase occurs in the peak of the action potential trace.

Record this maximal voltage here: _____ V

Click **Record Data** to record your results. ◼

Now that we have seen that an electrical impulse can cause an action potential, let's try some other methods of stimulating a nerve.

Activity 2:
Mechanical Stimulation

1. Click the **Clear** button on the oscilloscope.

2. Using the mouse, click the glass rod located on the bottom shelf on the left side of the screen, and drag it over to the nerve. When the glass rod is over the nerve, release the mouse button to indicate that the rod is now touching the nerve. What do you see on the oscilloscope screen?

_____

_____

How does this tracing compare with the other tracings that you have generated?

_____

_____

Click **Record Data** to record your results. Leave the graph on the screen so that you can compare it to the graph you will generate in the next activity. ◼

Activity 3:
Thermal Stimulation

Click on the glass rod, and drag it to the heater, releasing the mouse button. Click on the **Heat** button. When the rod turns red, indicating that it has been heated, click and drag the rod over the nerve and release the mouse button. What happens?

_____

_____

How does this trace compare to the trace that was generated with the unheated glass rod?

_____

_____

What explanation can you provide for this?

_____

_____

Click **Record Data** to record your results. Then click **Clear** to clear the oscilloscope screen for the next activity. ◼

Activity 4:
Chemical Stimulation

1. Click and drag the dropper from the bottle of sodium chloride (salt solution) over to the nerve in the chamber and then release the mouse button to dispense drops.

Does this generate an action potential? _____

2. Using your threshold voltage setting from Activity 1, stimulate the nerve.

Does this tracing differ from the original threshold stimulus

tracing? _____

Click **Record Data** to record your results.

3. Click the **Clean** button on top of the nerve chamber. This will return the nerve to its original (nonsalted) state. Click **Clear** to clear the oscilloscope screen.

4. Click and drag the dropper from the bottle of hydrochloric acid over to the nerve, and release the mouse button to dispense drops.

Does this generate an action potential? _____

Does this tracing differ from the one generated by the original

threshold stimulus? _____

Click **Record Data** to record your results.

5. Click on the **Clean** button on the nerve chamber to clean the chamber and return the nerve to its untouched state.

6. Click **Tools → Print Data** to print the data you have recorded for this experiment.

To summarize your experimental results, what kinds of stimuli can elicit an action potential?

_____

_____

_____ ◼

Inhibiting a Nerve Impulse

Numerous physical factors and chemical agents can impair the ability of nerve fibers to function. For example, deep pressure and cold temperature both block nerve impulse transmission by preventing local blood supply from reaching the nerve fibers. Local anesthetics, alcohol, and numerous other chemicals are also effective in blocking nerve transmission. In this experiment, we will study the effects of various agents on nerve transmission.

To begin, click the **Experiment** menu and select **Inhibiting a Nerve Impulse.** The display screen for this activity is similar to the screen in the first activity (Figure 3.4). To the left are bottles of several agents that we will test on the nerve. Keep the tracings you printed out from the first activity close at hand for comparison.

Activity 5:
Testing the Effects of Ether

1. Using the mouse, click and drag the dropper from the bottle of ether over to the nerve in between the stimulating electrodes and recording electrodes. Release the mouse button to dispense drops.

2. Using your threshold voltage setting from Activity 1, click **Stimulate.** What sort of trace do you see?

_____

What has happened to the nerve? _____

_____

Click **Record Data** to record your results.

Figure 3.4 Opening screen of the Inhibiting a Nerve Impulse experiment.

3. Click on the **Time (min)** button on the oscilloscope. The screen will now display activity over the course of 10 minutes (the space between each vertical line representing 1 minute). Because of the change in time scale, an action potential will look like a sharp vertical spike on the screen.

4. Click the (+) button under **Interval between Stimuli** on the stimulator until the timer is set for 2.0 minutes. This will set the stimulus to stimulate the nerve every two minutes. Click on **Stimulate** to start the stimulations. Watch the **Elapsed Time** display.

How long does it take for the nerve to return to normal?

_____

5. Click on the **Stop** button to stop this action and to return the Elapsed Time to 0.0.

6. Click the **Time (msec)** button on the oscilloscope to return it to its normal millisecond display.

7. Click **Clear** to clear the oscilloscope for the next activity.

8. Click the (−) button under **Interval between Stimuli** until it is reset to 0.00. ■

Activity 6:
Testing the Effects of Curare

Curare is a well-known plant extract that South American Indians used to paralyze their prey. It is an alpha-toxin that binds to acetylcholine binding sites on the postsynaptic cell membrane, which will prevent the acetylcholine from acting. Curare blocks synaptic transmission by preventing the flow of neural impulses from neuron to neuron.

1. Click and drag the dropper from the bottle of curare and position the dropper on the nerve in between the stimulating and recording electrodes. Release the mouse button to dispense drops.

2. Set the stimulator at the threshold voltage and stimulate the nerve. What effect on the action potential is noted?

_____

What explains this effect? _____

What do you think would be the overall effect of curare on the organism?

_____

_____

Click **Record Data** to record your results.

3. Click on the **Clean** button on the nerve chamber to remove the curare and return the nerve to its original untouched state.

4. Click **Clear** to clear the oscilloscope screen for the next activity. ▪

Activity 7:
Testing the Effects of Lidocaine

Note: Lidocaine is a sodium-channel antagonist.

1. Click and drag the dropper from the bottle of lidocaine and position it over the nerve between the stimulating and recording electrodes. Release the mouse button to dispense drops. Does this generate a trace?

_____

_____

2. Stimulate the nerve at the threshold voltage. What sort of tracing is seen?

_____

Why does lidocaine have this effect on nerve fiber transmission?

_____

_____

Click **Record Data** to record your results. Click **Tools** → **Print Data** if you wish to print your data.

3. Click on the **Clean** button on the nerve chamber to remove the lidocaine and return the nerve to its original untouched state. ▪

Nerve Conduction Velocity

As has been pointed out, one of the major physiological properties of neurons is conductivity: the ability to transmit the nerve impulse to other neurons, muscles, or glands. The nerve impulse, or propagated action potential, occurs when Na^+ floods into the neuron, causing the membrane to depolarize. Although this event is spoken of in electrical terms, and is measured using instruments that measure electrical events, the velocity of the action potential along a neural membrane does not occur at the speed of light. Rather, this event is much slower. In certain nerves in the human, the velocity of an action potential may be as fast as 120 meters per second. In other nerves, conduction speed is much slower, occurring at a speed of less than 3 meters per second.

To see the setup for this experiment, click the **Experiment** menu and select **Nerve Conduction Velocity** (Figure 3.5). In this exercise, the oscilloscope and stimulator will be used along with a third instrument, the bio-amplifier. The **bio-amplifier** is used to amplify any membrane depolarization so that the oscilloscope can easily record the event. Normally, when a membrane depolarization sufficient to initiate an action potential is looked at, the interior of the cell membrane goes from -70 mV to about $+40$ mV. This is easily registered and viewable on an oscilloscope without the aid of an amplifier. However, in this experiment, it is the change in the membrane potential on the _outside_ of the nerve that is being observed. The change that occurs here during depolarization will be so minuscule that it must be amplified in order to be visible on the oscilloscope.

A nerve chamber (similar to the one used in the previous two experiments) will be used. The design is basically a plastic box with platinum electrodes running across it. The nerve will be laid on these electrodes. Two electrodes will be used to bring the impulse from the stimulator to the nerve and three will be used for recording the membrane depolarization.

In this experiment, we will determine and compare the conduction velocities of different types of nerves. We will examine four nerves: an earthworm nerve, a frog nerve, and two rat nerves. The earthworm nerve is the smallest of the four. The frog nerve is a medium-sized myelinated nerve. Rat nerve 1 is a medium-sized unmyelinated nerve. Rat nerve 2 is a large, myelinated nerve—the largest nerve in this group. We will observe the effects of size and myelination on nerve conductivity.

The basic layout of the materials is shown in Figure 3.5. The two wires (red and black) from the stimulator connect with the top right side of the nerve chamber. Three recording wires (red, black, and a bare wire cable) are attached to connectors on the other end of the nerve chamber and go to the bio-amplifier. The bare cable serves as a ground reference for the electrical circuit and provides the reference for comparison of any change in membrane potential. The bio-amplifier is connected to the oscilloscope so that any amplified membrane changes can be observed. The stimulator output, called the _pulse,_ has been connected to the oscilloscope so that when the nerve is stimulated, the tracing will start across the oscilloscope screen. Thus, the time from the start of the trace on the left side of the screen (when the nerve was stimulated) to the actual nerve deflection (from the recording electrodes) can be accurately measured. This amount of time, usually in milliseconds, is critical for determining conduction velocity.

Figure 3.5 Opening screen of the Nerve Conduction Velocity experiment.

Activity 8:
Measuring Nerve Conduction Velocity

1. On the stimulator, click the **Pulse** button.

2. Turn the bio-amplifier on by clicking the horizontal bar on the bio-amplifier and dragging it to the **On** setting.

On the left side of the screen are the four nerves that will be studied. The nerves included are the earthworm, a frog nerve, and two rat nerves of different sizes. The earthworm as a whole is used because it has a nerve running down its ventral surface. A frog nerve is used as the frog has long been the animal of choice in many physiology laboratories. The rat nerves are used so that you may compare (a) the conduction velocity of different sized nerves and (b) the conduction velocity of a myelinated versus unmyelinated nerve. Remember that the frog nerve is myelinated and that rat nerve 1 is the same size as the frog nerve but unmyelinated. Rat nerve 2, the largest nerve of the bunch, is myelinated.

3. Using the mouse, click and drag the dropper from the bottle of ethanol over the earthworm and release the mouse

button to dispense drops of ethanol. This will narcotize the worm so it does not move around during the experiment but will not affect nerve conduction velocity. The alcohol is at a low enough percentage that the worm will be fine and back to normal within 15 minutes.

4. Click and drag the earthworm into the nerve chamber. Be sure the worm is over both of the stimulating electrodes and all three of the recording electrodes.

5. Using the (+) button next to the **Voltage** display, set the voltage to 1.0 V. Then click **Stimulate** to stimulate the nerve. Do you see an action potential? If not, increase the voltage by increments of 1.0 V until a trace is obtained.

At what threshold voltage do you first see an action potential

generated? _____ V

6. Next, click on the **Measure** button located on the stimulator. You will see a vertical yellow line appear on the far left edge of the oscilloscope screen. Now click the (+) button under the Measure button. This will move the yellow line to the right. This line lets you measure how much time has elapsed

on the graph at the point that the line is crossing the graph. You will see the elapsed time appear on the **Time (msec)** display on the stimulator. Keep clicking (+) until the yellow line is right at the point in the graph where the graph ceases being a flat line and first starts to rise.

7.   Once you have the yellow line positioned at the start of the graph's ascent, note the time elapsed at this point. Click **Record Data** to record the elapsed time on the data collection graph. PhysioEx will automatically compute the conduction velocity based on this data. Note that the data collection box includes a **Distance (mm)** column and that the distance is always 43 mm. This is the distance from the red stimulating wire to the red recording wire. In a wet lab, you would have to measure the distance yourself before you could proceed with calculating the conduction velocity.

It is important that you have the yellow vertical measuring line positioned at the start of the graph's rise before you click **Record Data**—otherwise, the conduction velocity calculated for the nerve will be inaccurate.

8.   Fill in the data under the Earthworm column on Chart 1 below.

9.   Click and drag the earthworm to its original place. Click **Clear** to clear the oscilloscope screen.

10.   Repeat steps 4 through 9 for the remaining nerves. Remember to click **Record Data** after each experimental run and to fill in the chart for question 8.

11.   Click **Tools → Print Data** to print your data.

Which nerve in the group has the slowest conduction velocity?

_____

What was the speed of the nerve? _____

Which nerve in the group of four has the fastest conduction velocity?

_____

What was the speed of the nerve? _____

What is the relationship between nerve size and conduction

velocity? _____

_____

_____

_____

Based on the results, what is your conclusion regarding conduction velocity and whether the nerve is myelinated or not?

_____

_____

_____

What is the major reason for the differences seen in conduction velocity between the myelinated nerves and the

unmyelinated nerves? _____

_____

_____

Histology Review Supplement

Turn to page 125 for a review of nervous tissue.

Chart 1

Nerve	Earthworm (small nerve)	Frog (medium nerve, myelinated)	Rat nerve 1 (medium nerve, unmyelinated)	Rat nerve 2 (large nerve, myelinated)
Threshold voltage				
Elapsed time from stimulation to action potential				
Conduction velocity				

Endocrine System Physiology

Objectives

1. To define the following terms: *metabolism, hormone replacement therapy, type I diabetes, type II diabetes,* and *glucose standard curve.*

2. To explain the role of thyroxine in maintaining an animal's metabolic rate.

3. To explain the effects of thyroid-stimulating hormone on an animal's metabolic rate.

4. To understand how estrogen affects uterine tissue growth.

5. To explain how hormone replacement therapy works.

6. To explain why insulin is important and how it can be used to treat diabetes.

The endocrine system exerts many complex and interrelated effects on the body as a whole, as well as on specific tissues and organs. Studying the effects of hormones on the body is difficult to do in a wet lab because experiments often take days, weeks, or even months to complete and are expensive. In addition, live animals may need to be sacrificed, and technically difficult surgical procedures are sometimes necessary. This computer simulation allows you to study the effects of given hormones on the body by using "virtual" animals rather than live ones. You can carry out delicate surgical techniques with the click of a button and complete experiments in a fraction of the time that it would take in an actual wet lab environment.

Hormones and Metabolism

Metabolism is the broad term used for all biochemical reactions occurring in the body. Metabolism involves *catabolism,* a process by which complex materials are broken down into simpler substances, usually with the aid of enzymes found in the body cells. Metabolism also involves *anabolism,* in which the smaller materials are built up by enzymes to build larger, more complex molecules. When larger molecules are made, energy is stored in the various bonds formed. When bonds are broken in catabolism, energy that was stored in the bonds is released for use by the cell. Some of the energy liberated may go into the formation of ATP, the energy-rich material used by the body to run itself. However, not all of the energy liberated goes into this pathway; some is given off as body heat. Humans are *homeothermic* animals, meaning they have a fixed body temperature. Maintaining this temperature is important to maintaining the metabolic pathways found in the body.

The most important hormone in maintaining metabolism and body heat is *thyroxine,* the hormone of the thyroid gland, which is found in the neck. The thyroid gland secretes thyroxine, but the production of thyroxine is really controlled by the pituitary gland, which secretes *thyroid-stimulating hormone (TSH).* TSH is carried by the blood to the thyroid gland (its *target tissue*) and causes the thyroid to produce more thyroxine. So in an indirect way, an animal's metabolic rate is the result of pituitary hormones.

Figure 4.1   Opening screen of the Metabolism experiment.

In the following experiments, you will investigate the effects of thyroxine and TSH on an animal's metabolic rate. To begin, select **Endocrine System Physiology** from the main menu. The opening screen will appear in a few seconds (see Figure 4.1). Select **Balloons On** from the **Help** menu for help identifying the equipment onscreen (you will see labels appear as you roll the mouse over each piece of equipment). Select **Balloons Off** to turn this feature off before you begin the experiments.

Study the screen. You will see a jar-shaped chamber to the left, connected to a *respirometer-manometer apparatus* (consisting of a U-shaped tube, a syringe, and associated tubing.) You will be placing animals—in this case, rats—in the chamber in order to gather information about how thyroxine and TSH affect their metabolic rates. Note that the chamber also includes a weight scale, and under the timer is a weight display. Next to the chamber is a timer for setting and timing the length of a given experiment.

Two tubes are connected to the top of the chamber. The left tube has a clamp on it that can be opened or closed. Leaving the clamp open allows outside air into the chamber; closing the clamp creates a closed, airtight system. The other tube

leads to a *T-connector*. One branch of the T leads to a fluid-containing U-shaped tube, called a *manometer*. As an animal uses up the air in the closed system, this fluid will rise in the left side of the U-shaped tube and fall in the right.

The other branch of the T-connector leads to a syringe filled with air. Using the syringe to inject air into the tube, you will measure the amount of air that is needed to return the fluid columns to their original levels. This measurement will be equal to the amount of oxygen used by the animal during the elapsed time of the experiment. Soda lime, found at the bottom of the chamber, absorbs the carbon dioxide given off by the animal so that the amount of oxygen used can easily be measured. The amount of oxygen used by the animal, along with its weight, will be used to calculate the animal's metabolic rate.

Also on the screen are three white rats in their individual cages. These are the specimens you will use in the following experiments. One rat is *normal;* the second is *thyroidectomized* (abbreviated on the screen as *Tx*)— meaning its thyroid has been removed; and the third is *hypophysectomized* (abbreviated on the screen as *Hypox*), meaning its pituitary gland has been removed. The pituitary gland is also known as the *hypophysis,* and removal of this organ is called a *hypophysectomy.*

To the top left of the screen are three syringes with various chemicals inside: propylthiouracil, thyroid-stimulating hormone (TSH), and thyroxine. TSH and thyroxine have been previously mentioned; propylthiouracil is a drug that inhibits the production of thyroxine. You will perform four experiments on each animal to: (1) determine its baseline metabolic rate, (2) determine its metabolic rate after it has been injected with thyroxine, (3) determine its metabolic rate after it has been injected with TSH, and (4) determine its metabolic rate after it has been injected with propylthiouracil.

You will be recording all of your data on Chart 1 below. You may also record your data onscreen by using the equipment in the lower part of the screen, called the *data collection unit.* This equipment records and displays data you accumulate during the experiments. Check that the data set for **Normal** is highlighted in the **Data Sets** window since you will be experimenting with the normal rat first. The **Record Data** button lets you record data after an experimental trial. Clicking the **Delete Line** or **Clear Data Set** buttons erases any data you want to delete.

Activity 1:
Determining Baseline Metabolic Rates

First, you will determine the baseline metabolic rate for each rat.

1. Using the mouse, click and drag the **normal** rat into the chamber and place it on top of the scale. When the animal is in the chamber, release the mouse button.

Chart 1	Effects of Hormones on Metabolic Rate		
	Normal rat	**Thyroidectomized rat**	**Hypophysectomized rat**
Baseline			
Weight	_____ grams	_____ grams	_____ grams
ml O_2 used in 1 minute	_____ ml	_____ ml	_____ ml
ml O_2 used per hour	_____ ml	_____ ml	_____ ml
Metabolic rate	_____ ml O_2/kg/hr	_____ ml O_2/kg/hr	_____ ml O_2/kg/hr
With thyroxine			
Weight	_____ grams	_____ grams	_____ grams
ml O_2 used in 1 minute	_____ ml	_____ ml	_____ ml
ml O_2 used per hour	_____ ml	_____ ml	_____ ml
Metabolic rate	_____ ml O_2/kg/hr	_____ ml O_2/kg/hr	_____ ml O_2/kg/hr
With TSH			
Weight	_____ grams	_____ grams	_____ grams
ml O_2 used in 1 minute	_____ ml	_____ ml	_____ ml
ml O_2 used per hour	_____ ml	_____ ml	_____ ml
Metabolic rate	_____ ml O_2/kg/hr	_____ ml O_2/kg/hr	_____ ml O_2/kg/hr
With propylthiouracil			
Weight	_____ grams	_____ grams	_____ grams
ml O_2 used in 1 minute	_____ ml	_____ ml	_____ ml
ml O_2 used per hour	_____ ml	_____ ml	_____ ml
Metabolic rate	_____ ml O_2/kg/hr	_____ ml O_2/kg/hr	_____ ml O_2/kg/hr

2. Be sure the clamp on the left tube (on top of the chamber) is open, allowing air to enter the chamber. If the clamp is closed, click on it to open it.

3. Be sure the indicator next to the T-connector reads "Chamber and manometer connected." If not, click on the **T-connector knob.**

4. Click on the **Weigh** button in the box to the right of the chamber to weigh the rat. Record this weight in the Baseline section of Chart 1 in the row labeled "Weight."

5. Click the (**+**) button on the **Timer** so that the Timer display reads 1 minute.

6. Click on the clamp to close it. This will prevent any outside air from entering the chamber and ensure that the only oxygen the rat is breathing is the oxygen inside the closed system.

7. Click **Start** on the Timer display. You will see the elapsed time appear in the "Elapsed Time" display. Watch what happens to the water levels in the U-shaped tube.

8. At the end of the 1-minute period, the timer will automatically stop. When it stops, click on the **T-connector knob** so that the indicator reads "Manometer and syringe connected."

9. Click on the clamp to open it so that the rat can once again breathe outside air.

10. Click the (**+**) button under ml O_2 so that the display reads "1.0". Then click **Inject,** and watch what happens to the fluid levels. Continue clicking the (**+**) button and injecting air until the fluid in the two arms of the U-tube are level again. How many milliliters of air need to be added to equalize the fluid in the two arms? (This is equivalent to the amount of oxygen that the rat used up during 1 minute in the closed chamber.) Record this measurement in the Baseline section of Chart 1 in the row labeled "ml O_2 used in 1 minute."

11. Determine the oxygen consumption per hour for the rat. Use the following formula:

$$\frac{\text{ml } O_2 \text{ consumed}}{1 \text{ minute}} \times \frac{60 \text{ minutes}}{1 \text{ hr}} = \text{ml } O_2/\text{hr}$$

Record this data in the Baseline section of the chart in the row labeled "ml O_2 used per hour."

12. Now that you have the amount of oxygen used per hour, determine the metabolic rate per kilogram of body weight by using the following formula. (Note that you will need to convert the weight data from g to kg before you can use the formula.)

$$\text{Metabolic Rate} = \frac{\text{ml } O_2/\text{hr}}{\text{wt. in kg}} = \underline{\hspace{1.5cm}} \text{ml } O_2/\text{kg/hr}$$

Record this data in the Baseline section of the chart in the row labeled "Metabolic rate."

13. Click **Record Data.**

14. Click and drag the rat from the chamber back to its cage.

15. Click the **Reset** button in the box labeled *Apparatus.*

16. Now repeat steps 1–15 for the **thyroidectomized (Tx)** and **hypophysectomized (Hypox)** rats. Record your data in the Baseline section of the chart under the corresponding column for each rat. Be sure to highlight **Tx** under **Data Sets**

(on the data collection box) before beginning the experiment on the thyroidectomized rat; likewise, highlight **Hypox** under **Data Sets** before beginning the experiment on the hypophysectomized rat.

How did the metabolic rates of the three rats differ?

_____

_____

_____

Why did the metabolic rates differ?

_____

_____

_____ ■

Activity 2:
Determining the Effect of Thyroxine on Metabolic Rate

Next, you will investigate the effects of thyroxine injections on the metabolic rates of all three rats.

Note that in a wet lab environment, you would normally need to inject thyroxine (or any other hormone) into a rat *daily* for a minimum of 1–2 weeks in order for any response to be seen. However, in the following simulations, you will inject the rat only once and be able to witness the same results as if you had administered multiple injections over the course of several weeks. In addition, by clicking the **Clean** button while a rat is inside its cage, you can magically remove all residue of any previously injected hormone from the rat and perform a new experiment on the same rat. In a real wet lab environment, you would need to either wait weeks for hormonal residue to leave the rat's system or use a different rat.

1. Select a rat to test. You will eventually test all three, and it doesn't matter in what order you test them. Under **Data Sets,** highlight **Normal, Tx,** or **Hypox** depending on which rat you select.

2. Click the **Reset** button in the box labeled *Apparatus.*

3. Click on the syringe labeled **thyroxine** and drag it over to the rat. Release the mouse button. This will cause thyroxine to be injected into the rat.

4. Click and drag the rat into the chamber. Perform steps 1–12 of Activity 1 again, except this time record your data in the With Thyroxine section of the chart.

5. Click **Record Data.**

6. Click and drag the rat from the chamber back to its cage, and click **Clean** to cleanse it of all traces of thyroxine.

7. Now repeat steps 1–6 for the remaining rats. Record your data in the With Thyroxine section of the chart under the corresponding column for each rat.

What was the effect of thyroxine on the normal rat's metabolic rate? How does it compare to the normal rat's baseline metabolic rate?

_____

_____

Why was this effect seen? _____

_____

What was the effect of thyroxine on the thyroidectomized rat's metabolic rate? How does it compare to the thyroidectomized rat's baseline metabolic rate?

_____

_____

_____

Why was this effect seen? _____

_____

What was the effect of thyroxine on the hypophysectomized rat's metabolic rate? How does it compare to the hypophysectomized rat's baseline metabolic rate?

_____

_____

_____

Why was this effect seen? _____

_____ ■

Activity 3:
Determining the Effect of TSH on Metabolic Rate

Now you will investigate the effects of TSH injections on the metabolic rates of the three rats. Select a rat to experiment on first, and then proceed.

1.   Under **Data Sets,** highlight **Normal, Tx,** or **Hypox,** depending on which rat you are using.

2.   Click the **Reset** button in the box labeled *Apparatus*.

3.   Click and drag the syringe labeled **TSH** over to the rat and release the mouse button, injecting the rat.

4.   Click and drag the rat into the chamber. Perform steps 1–12 of Activity 1 again. Record your data in the With TSH section of the chart.

5.   Click **Record Data.**

6.   Click and drag the rat from the chamber back to its cage, and click **Clean** to cleanse it of all traces of TSH.

7.   Now repeat this activity for the remaining rats. Record your data in the With TSH section of the chart under the corresponding column for each rat.

What was the effect of TSH on the normal rat's metabolic rate? How does it compare to the normal rat's baseline metabolic rate?

_____

_____

_____

Why was this effect seen? _____

_____

What was the effect of TSH on the thyroidectomized rat's metabolic rate? How does it compare to the thyroidectomized rat's baseline metabolic rate?

_____

_____

_____

Why was this effect seen? _____

_____

What was the effect of TSH on the hypophysectomized rat's metabolic rate? How does it compare to the hypophysectomized rat's baseline metabolic rate?

_____

_____

_____

Why was this effect seen? _____

_____ ■

Activity 4:
Determining the Effect of Propylthiouracil on Metabolic Rate

Next, you will investigate the effects of propylthiouracil injections on the metabolic rates of the three rats. Keep in mind that propylthiouracil is a drug that inhibits the production of thyroxine. Select a rat to experiment on first, and then proceed.

1.   Under **Data Sets,** highlight **Normal, Tx,** or **Hypox,** depending on which rat you are using.

Endocrine System Physiology

2. Click the **Reset** button in the box labeled *Apparatus*.

3. Click and drag the syringe labeled **propylthiouracil** over to the rat and release the mouse button, injecting the rat.

4. Click and drag the rat into the chamber. Perform steps 1–12 of Activity 1 again, except this time record your data in the With Propylthiouracil section of the chart.

5. Click **Record Data.**

6. Click and drag the rat from the chamber back to its cage, and click **Clean** to cleanse the rat of all traces of propylthiouracil.

7. Now repeat this activity for the remaining rats. Record your data in the With Propylthiouracil section of the chart under the corresponding column for each rat.

What was the effect of propylthiouracil on the normal rat's metabolic rate? How does it compare to the normal rat's baseline metabolic rate?

_____

_____

_____

Why was this effect seen? _____

_____

What was the effect of propylthiouracil on the thyroidectomized rat's metabolic rate? How does it compare to the thyroidectomized rat's baseline metabolic rate?

_____

_____

_____

Why was this effect seen? _____

_____

What was the effect of propylthiouracil on the hypophysectomized rat's metabolic rate? How does it compare to the hypophysectomized rat's baseline metabolic rate?

_____

_____

_____

Why was this effect seen? _____

_____

8. If you wish, click **Tools → Print Data** to print all of your recorded data for this experiment. ■

Hormone Replacement Therapy

Follicle-stimulating hormone (FSH) stimulates ovarian follicle growth. While the follicles are developing, they produce the hormone *estrogen*. One target tissue for estrogen is the uterus. The action of estrogen is to enable the endometrium of the uterus to grow and develop so that the uterus may receive fertilized eggs for implantation. *Ovariectomy,* the removal of ovaries, will remove the source of estrogen and cause the uterus to slowly atrophy.

In this activity, you will re-create a classic endocrine experiment and examine how estrogen affects uterine tissue growth. You will be working with two female rats, both of which have been ovariectomized and are thus no longer producing estrogen. You will administer **hormone replacement therapy** to one rat by giving it daily injections of estrogen. The other rat will serve as your control and receive daily injections of saline. You will then remove the uterine tissues from both rats, weigh the tissues, and compare them to determine the effects of hormone replacement therapy.

Start by selecting **Hormone Replacement Therapy** from the **Experiment** menu. A new screen will appear (Figure 4.2) with the two ovariectomized rats in cages. (Note that if this were a wet lab, the ovariectomies would need to have been performed on the rats a month prior to the rest of the experiment in order to ensure that no residual hormones remained in the rats' systems.) Also on screen are a bottle of saline, a bottle of estrogen, a syringe, a box of weighing paper, and a weighing scale.

Proceed carefully with this experiment. Each rat will disappear from the screen once you remove its uterus, and it cannot be brought back unless you restart the experiment. This replicates the situation you would encounter if working with live animals: once the uterus is removed, the animal would have to be sacrificed.

Activity 5:
Hormone Replacement Therapy

1. Click on the syringe, drag it to the bottle of **saline,** and release the mouse button. The syringe will automatically fill with 1 ml of saline.

2. Drag the syringe to the **control** rat and place the tip of the needle in the rat's lower abdominal area. Injections into this area are considered *interperitoneal* and will quickly be picked up by the abdominal blood vessels. Release the mouse button—the syringe will empty into the rat and automatically return to its holder. Click **Clean** on the syringe holder to clean the syringe of all residue.

3. Click on the syringe again, this time dragging it to the bottle of **estrogen,** and release the mouse button. The syringe will automatically fill with 1 ml of estrogen.

4. Drag the syringe to the **experimental** rat and place the tip of the needle in the rat's lower abdominal area. Release the mouse button—the syringe will empty into the rat and automatically return to its holder. Click **Clean** on the syringe holder to clean the syringe of all residue.

Figure 4.2 Opening screen of the Hormone Replacement Therapy experiment.

5. Click on the **Clock.** You will notice the hands sweep the clock face twice, indicating that 24 hours have passed.

6. Repeat steps 1–5 until each rat has received a total of 7 injections over the course of 7 days (1 injection per day). Note that the **# of injections** displayed below each rat cage records how many injections the rat has received. The control rat should receive 7 injections of saline, whereas the experimental rat should receive 7 injections of estrogen.

7. Next, click on the box of weighing paper. You will see a small piece of paper appear. Click and drag this paper over to the top of the scale and release the mouse button.

8. Notice the scale will give you a weight for the paper. With the mouse arrow, click on the **Tare** button to tare the scale to zero (0.0000 gms), adjusting for the weight of the paper.

9. You are now ready to remove the uteruses. In a wet lab, this would require surgery. Here, you will simply click on the **Remove Uterus** button found in each rat cage. The rats will disappear, and a uterus (consisting of a uterine body and two uterine horns) will appear in each cage.

10. Click and drag the uterus from the **control** rat over to the scale and release it on the weighing paper. Click on the **Weigh** button to obtain the weight. Record the weight here:

Uterus weight (control): _____ gms

11. Click **Record Data.**

12. Click **Clean** on the weight scale to dispense of the weighing paper and uterus.

13. Repeat steps 7 and 8. Then click and drag the uterus from the **experimental** rat over to the scale and release it on the weighing paper. Click **Weigh** to obtain the weight. Record the weight here:

Uterus weight (experimental): _____ gms

14. Click **Record Data.**

15. Click **Clean** on the weight scale to dispense of the weighing paper and uterus.

16. Click **Tools → Print Data** to print your recorded data for this experiment.

How does the control uterus weight compare to the experimental uterus weight?

_____

_____

What can you conclude about the administration of estrogen injections on the experimental animal?

_____

_____

_____

What might be the effect if testosterone had been administered instead of estrogen? Explain your answer.

_____

_____

_____ ∎

Insulin and Diabetes

Insulin is produced by the beta cells of the endocrine portion of the pancreas. It is vital to the regulation of blood glucose levels because it enables the body's cells to absorb glucose from the bloodstream. When insulin is not produced by the pancreas, **diabetes mellitus type I** results. When insulin is produced by the pancreas but the body fails to respond to it, **diabetes mellitus type II** results. In either case, glucose remains in the bloodstream, unable to be taken up by the body's cells to serve as the primary fuel for metabolism.

In the following experiment, you will study the effects of insulin treatment for type I diabetes. The experiment is divided into two parts. In Part I, you will obtain a _glucose standard curve,_ which will be explained shortly. In Part II, you will compare the glucose levels of a normal rat to those of a diabetic rat, and then compare them again after each rat has been injected with insulin.

Part I

Activity 6:
Obtaining a Glucose Standard Curve

To begin, select **Insulin and Diabetes-Part 1** from the **Experiments** menu (see Figure 4.3).

Select **Balloons On** from the Help menu for help identifying the equipment onscreen. (You will see labels appear as you roll the mouse over each piece of equipment.) Select **Balloons Off** to turn this feature off before you begin the experiments.

On the right side of the opening screen is a special spectrophotometer. The **spectrophotometer** is one of the most widely used research instruments in biology. It is used to measure the amounts of light of different wavelengths absorbed and transmitted by a pigmented solution. Inside the spectrophotometer is a source for white light, which is separated into various wavelengths (or colors) by a prism. The user selects a wavelength (color), and light of this color is passed through a special tube, or _cuvette,_ containing the sample being

tested. (For this experiment, the spectrophotometer light source will be preset for a wavelength of 450 nano-meters, or nm.) The light transmitted by the sample then passes onto a photoelectric tube, which converts the light energy into an electrical current. The current is then measured by a meter. Alternatively, the light may be measured before the sample is put into the light path, and the amount of light absorbed—called **optical density**—is measured. Using either method, the change in light transmittance or light absorbed can be used to measure the amount of a given substance in the sample being tested.

In Part II, you will use the spectrophotometer to determine how much glucose is present in blood samples taken from two rats. Before using the spectrophotometer, you must obtain a **glucose standard curve** so that you have a point of reference for converting optical density readings into glucose readings, which will be measured in mg/deciliter (mg/dl). To do this, you will prepare five test tubes that contain known amounts of glucose: 30 mg/dl, 60 mg/dl, 90 mg/dl, 120 mg/dl, and 150 mg/dl, respectively. You will then use the spectrophotometer to determine the corresponding optical density readings for each of these known amounts of glucose. Information obtained in Part I will be used to perform Part II.

Also on the screen are three dropper bottles, a test tube washer, a test tube dispenser (on top of the washer), and a test tube incubation unit with numbered cradles that you will need to prepare the samples for analysis.

1. Click and drag the test tube (on top of the test tube washer) into slot 1 of the incubation unit. You will see another test tube pop up from the dispenser. Click and drag this second test tube into slot 2 of the incubation unit. Repeat until you have dragged a total of five test tubes into the five slots in the incubation unit.

2. Click and hold the mouse button on the dropper cap of the **glucose standard** bottle. Drag the dropper cap over to tube 1. Release the mouse button to dispense the glucose. You will see that one drop of glucose solution is dropped into the tube and that the dropper cap automatically returns to the bottle of glucose standard.

3. Repeat step 2 with the remaining four tubes. Notice that each subsequent tube will automatically receive one additional drop of glucose standard into the tube (i.e., tube 2 will receive two drops, tube 3 will receive three drops, tube 4 will receive four drops, and tube 5 will receive five drops).

4. Click and hold the mouse button on the dropper cap of the **deionized water** bottle. Drag the dropper cap over to tube 1. Release the mouse button to dispense the water. Notice that four drops of water are automatically added to the first tube.

5. Repeat step 4 with tubes 2, 3, and 4. Notice that each subsequent tube will receive one _less_ drop of water than the previous tube (i.e., tube 2 will receive three drops, tube 3 will receive two drops, and tube 4 will receive one drop. Tube 5 will receive _no_ drops of water.)

6. Click on the **Mix** button of the incubator to mix the contents of the tubes.

7. Click on the **Centrifuge** button. The tubes will descend into the incubator and be centrifuged.

8. When the tubes resurface, click on the **Remove Pellet** button. Any pellets from the centrifuging process will be removed from the test tubes.

Figure 4.3 **Opening screen of the Insulin and Diabetes experiment, Part I.**

9. Click and hold the mouse button on the dropper cap of the **enzyme-color reagent** bottle. Still holding the mouse button down, drag the dropper cap over to tube 1. When you release the mouse, you will note that five drops of reagent are added to the tube and that the stopper is returned to its bottle.

10. Repeat step 9 for the remaining tubes.

11. Now click **Incubate.** The tubes will descend into the incubator, incubate, and then resurface.

12. Using the mouse, click on **Set Up** on the spectrophotometer. This will warm up the instrument and get it ready for your readings.

13. Click and drag tube 1 into the spectrophotometer (right above the **Set Up** button) and release the mouse button. The tube will lock into place.

14. Click **Analyze.** You will see a spot appear on the screen and values appear in the **Optical Density** and **Glucose** displays.

15. Click **Record Data** on the data collection unit.

16. Click and drag the tube into the test tube washer.

17. Repeat steps 13–16 for the remaining test tubes.

18. When all five tubes have been analyzed, click on the **Graph** button. This is the glucose standard graph, which you will use in Part II of the experiment. Click **Tools → Print Data** to print your recorded data. ■

Part II

Activity 7:

Comparing Glucose Levels Before and After Insulin Injection

Select **Insulin and Diabetes-Part 2** from the **Experiments** menu.

The opening screen will look similar to the screen from Part I (Figure 4.4). Notice the two rats in their cages. One will be your control animal, the other your experimental animal. Also note the three syringes, containing insulin, saline, and alloxan, respectively. **Alloxan** is a rather nasty drug: When administered to an animal, it will selectively kill all the cells that produce insulin and render the animal instantly diabetic. It does this by destroying the beta cells of the pancreas, which are responsible for insulin production.

Figure 4.4 Opening screen of the Insulin and Diabetes experiment, Part II.

In this experiment, you will inject the control rat with saline and the experimental rat with alloxan. (Normally, injections are given *daily* for a week. In this simulation, we will administer the injections only once but will be able to see results as though the injections had been given over a longer period of time.)

After administering the saline and alloxan injections, you will obtain blood samples from the two rats. You will then inject both rats with insulin, and obtain blood samples again. Finally, you will analyze all the blood samples in the spectrophotometer (described in Part I) comparing the amounts of glucose present.

1.   Click and drag the **saline** syringe to the **control** rat, and release the mouse button to inject the animal.

2.   Click and drag the **alloxan** syringe to the **experimental** rat, and release the mouse button to inject the animal.

3.   Click and drag a new test tube (from the test tube dispenser) over to the tail of the **control** rat, and release the mouse button. You will note three drops of blood being drawn from the tail into the tube. Next, click and drag the tube into test tube holder 1 in the incubator. (**Note:** The tail is a popular

place to get blood from a rat. The end of the tail can easily be clipped and blood collected without really disturbing the rat. The tail heals quickly with no harm to the animal.)

4.   Click and drag another new test tube (from the test tube dispenser) over to the tail of the **experimental** rat, and release the mouse button. Again, you will note that three drops of blood are drawn from the tail into the tube. Click and drag the tube into test tube holder 2 in the incubator.

5.   Click and drag the **insulin** syringe to the **control** rat, and release the mouse button to inject the animal.

6.   Repeat step 5 with the **experimental** rat.

7.   Repeat steps 3 and 4 again, drawing blood samples from each rat and placing the samples into test tube holders 3 and 4.

8.   Click the **Obtain Reagents** button on the cabinet that currently displays the syringes. The syringes will disappear, and you will see four dropper bottles in their place.

9.   Click and hold the mouse button on the dropper of the **deionized water** bottle. Drag the dropper cap over to tube 1. Release the mouse button to dispense. You will note that five drops of water are added to the tube.

10. Repeat step 9 for the remaining test tubes.

11. Click and hold the mouse button on the dropper of the **barium hydroxide.** Drag the dropper cap over to tube 1. Release the mouse button to dispense. Note that five drops of solution are added to the tube. (Barium hydroxide is used for clearing proteins and cells so that clear glucose readings may be obtained.)

12. Repeat step 11 for the remaining test tubes.

13. Click and hold the mouse button on the dropper of the **heparin** bottle. Still holding the mouse button down, drag the dropper cap over to tube 1. Release the mouse button to dispense. (Heparin is an anticoagulant that prevents blood clotting.)

14. Repeat step 13 for the remaining test tubes.

15. Click on the **Mix** button of the incubator to mix the contents of the tubes.

16. Click on the **Centrifuge** button. The tubes will descend into the incubator, be centrifuged, and then resurface.

17. Click on the **Remove Pellet** button to remove any pellets from the centrifuging process.

18. Click and hold the mouse button on the dropper of the **enzyme-color reagent** bottle. Drag the dropper cap to tube 1. Release the mouse to dispense.

19. Repeat step 18 with the remaining test tubes. In an actual wet lab, you would also shake the test tubes after adding the enzyme-color reagent.

20. Click **Incubate** one more time. The tubes will descend into the incubator, incubate, and then resurface.

21. Click on **Set Up** on the spectrophotometer to warm up the instrument and get it ready for your readings.

22. Click **Graph Glucose Standard.** The graph from Part I of the experiment will appear on the monitor.

23. Click and drag tube 1 to the spectrophotometer and release the mouse button. The tube will lock into place.

24. Click **Analyze.** You will see a horizontal line appear on the screen and a value appear in the **Optical Density** display.

25. Drag the movable rule (the vertical line on the far right of the spectrophotometer monitor) over to where the horizontal line (from step 24) crosses the glucose standard line. Watch what happens to the Glucose display as you move the movable rule to the left.

What is the glucose reading where the horizontal line crosses the glucose standard line?

Test tube 1: _____ mg/dl glucose

This is your glucose reading for the sample being tested.

26. Click **Record Data** on the data collection unit.

27. Click and drag the test tube from the spectrophotometer into the test tube washer, then click **Clear** underneath the oscilloscope display.

28. Repeat steps 22–27 for the remaining test tubes. Record your glucose readings for each test tube here:

Test tube 2: _____ mg/dl glucose

Test tube 3: _____ mg/dl glucose

Test tube 4: _____ mg/dl glucose

How does the glucose level in test tube 1 compare to the level in test tube 2? Recall that tube 1 contains a sample from your control rat (which received injections of saline) and that tube 2 contains a sample from your experimental rat (which received injections of alloxan).

_____

Explain this result. _____

_____

What is the condition that alloxan has caused in the experimental rat?

_____

How does the glucose level in test tube 3 compare to the level in test tube 1?

_____

Explain this result. _____

_____

How does the glucose level in test tube 4 compare to the level in test tube 2?

_____

Explain this result. _____

_____

What was the effect of administering insulin to the control animal?

_____

What was the effect of administering insulin to the experimental animal?

_____ ■

29. Click **Tools → Print Data** to print your recorded data.

Histology Review Supplement

Turn to page 126 for a review of endocrine tissue.

Cardiovascular Dynamics

The physiology of human blood circulation can be divided into two distinct but remarkably harmonized processes: (1) the pumping of blood by the heart, and (2) the transport of blood to all body tissues via the vasculature, or blood vessels. Blood supplies all body tissues with the substances needed for survival, so it is vital that blood delivery is ample for tissue demands.

The Mechanics of Circulation

To understand how blood is transported throughout the body, let's examine three important factors influencing how blood circulates through the cardiovascular system: blood flow, blood pressure, and peripheral resistance.

Blood flow is the amount of blood moving through a body area or the entire cardiovascular system in a given amount of time. While total blood flow is determined by cardiac output (the amount of blood the heart is able to pump per minute), blood flow to specific body areas can vary dramatically in a given time period. Organs differ in their requirements from moment to moment, and blood vessels constrict or dilate to regulate local blood flow to various areas in response to the tissues' immediate needs. Consequently, blood flow can increase to some regions and decrease to other areas at the same time.

Blood pressure is the force blood exerts against the wall of a blood vessel. Owing to cardiac activity, pressure is highest at the heart end of any artery. Because of the effect of peripheral resistance, which will be discussed shortly, pressure within the arteries (or any blood vessel) drops as the distance (vessel length) from the heart increases. This pressure gradient causes blood to move from and then back to the heart, always moving from high- to low-pressure areas.

Peripheral resistance is the opposition to blood flow resulting from the friction developed as blood streams through blood vessels. Three factors affect vessel resistance: blood viscosity, vessel radius, and vessel length.

Blood viscosity is a measure of the "thickness" of the blood, and is caused by the presence of proteins and formed elements in the plasma (the fluid part of the blood). As the viscosity of a fluid increases, its flow rate through a tube decreases. Blood viscosity in healthy people normally does not change, but certain conditions such as too many or too few blood cells may modify it.

Objectives

1. To define the following terms: *blood flow, peripheral resistance, viscosity, systole, diastole, end diastolic volume, end systolic volume, stroke volume,* and *cardiac output.*

2. To explore cardiovascular dynamics using an experimental setup to simulate a human body function.

3. To understand that heart and blood vessel functions are highly coordinated.

4. To comprehend that pressure differences provide the driving force that moves blood through the blood vessels.

5. To recognize that body tissues may differ in their blood demands at a given time.

6. To identify the most important factors in control of blood flow.

7. To comprehend that changing blood vessel diameter can alter the pumping ability of the heart.

8. To examine the effect of stroke volume on blood flow.

Circle the correct term within the parentheses: Because fluid flow is proportional to the fourth power of the radius, (increases / decreases) in tube radius cause (increases / decreases) in fluid flow.

Is the relationship between fluid flow and flow tube radius linear or exponential? _____

In this experiment, a simulated motor changes the diameter of the flow tube. Explain how our blood vessels alter blood flow.

_____

_____

_____

_____

After a heavy meal when we are relatively inactive, we might expect blood vessels in the skeletal muscles to be somewhat

_____, whereas blood vessels in the digestive

organs are probably _____. ■

Activity 2:
Studying the Effect of Viscosity on Fluid Flow

With a viscosity of 3 to 4, blood is much more viscous than water (1.0 viscosity). Although viscosity is altered by factors such as dehydration and altered blood cell numbers, a body in homeostatic balance has a relatively stable blood consistency. Nonetheless it is useful to examine the effects of viscosity changes on fluid flow because we can then predict what might transpire in the human cardiovascular system under certain homeostatic imbalances.

1.   Set the starting conditions as follows:

• 100 mm Hg driving pressure
• 5.0-mm flow tube radius
• 1.0 viscosity
• 50-mm flow tube length

2.   Click the **Viscosity** data set in the data collection unit. (This action prepares the experimental values grid to record the viscosity data.)

3.   **Refill** the left beaker if you have not already done so.

4.   Click **Start** to begin the experiment. After all the fluid has drained into the right beaker, click **Record Data** to record this data point, and then click **Refill** to replenish the left beaker.

5.   In 1.0-unit increments, increase the fluid viscosity by clicking (**+**) next to the **Viscosity** window, and repeat step 4 until the maximum viscosity (10.0) is reached.

6.   View your data graphically by choosing **Plot Data** from the **Tools** menu. Choose **Viscosity** as the data set to be graphed, and then use the slider bars to select the viscosity data to be plotted on the X-axis and the flow data to be plotted on the Y-axis. You can highlight individual data points by clicking a line in the data grid. When finished, click the close box at the top of the plot window.

How does fluid flow change as viscosity is modified?

_____

_____

_____

Is fluid flow versus viscosity an inverse or direct relationship?

_____

How does the effect of viscosity compare with the effect of radius on fluid flow?

_____

_____

Predict the effect of anemia (e.g., fewer red blood cells than normal) on blood flow.

_____

_____

What might happen to blood flow if we increased the number of blood cells?

_____

_____

_____

Explain why changing blood viscosity would or would not be a reasonable method for the body to control blood flow.

_____

_____

_____

_____

Blood viscosity would _____ in conditions of

dehydration, resulting in _____ blood flow. ■

Activity 3:
Studying the Effect of Flow Tube Length on Fluid Flow

With the exception of the normal growth that occurs until the body reaches full maturity, blood vessel length does not significantly change. In this activity you will investigate the physical relationship between vessel length and blood movement; specifically, how blood flow changes in flow tubes (vessels) of constant radius but of different lengths.

1.   Set the starting conditions as follows:

*   100 mm Hg driving pressure
*   5.0-mm flow tube radius
*   3.5 viscosity
*   10-mm flow tube length

2.   Click the **Length** data set in the data collection unit. (This action prepares the experimental values grid to display the length data.)

3.   **Refill** the left beaker if you have not already done so.

4.   Click **Start** to begin the experiment. After all the fluid has drained into the right beaker, click **Record Data** to record this data point, and then click **Refill** to refill the left beaker.

5.   In 5-mm increments, increase the flow tube length by clicking (+) next to the **Length** window, and repeat step 4 until the maximum length (50 mm) has been reached.

6.   View your data graphically by choosing **Plot Data** from the **Tools** menu. Choose **Length** as the data set to be graphed, and then use the slider bars to select the length data to be plotted on the X-axis and the flow data to be plotted on the Y-axis. You can highlight individual data points by clicking a line in the grid. When finished, click the close box at the top of the plot window.

How does flow tube length affect fluid flow?

_____

_____

_____

Explain why altering blood vessel length would or would not be a good method of controlling blood flow in the body.

_____

_____

_____

Activity 4:
Studying the Effect of Pressure on Fluid Flow

The pressure difference between the two ends of a blood vessel is the driving force behind blood flow. In comparison, our experimental setup pressurizes the left beaker, thereby providing the driving force that propels fluid through the flow tube to the right beaker. You will examine the effect of pressure on fluid flow in this part of the experiment.

1.   Set the starting conditions as follows:

*   25 mm Hg driving pressure
*   5.0-mm flow tube radius
*   3.5 viscosity
*   50-mm flow tube length

2.   Click the **Pressure** data set in the data collection unit. (This action prepares the experimental values grid for the pressure data.)

3.   **Refill** the left beaker if you have not already done so.

4.   Click **Start** to begin the experiment. After all the fluid has moved into the right beaker, click **Record Data** to record this data point. Click **Refill** to refill the left beaker.

5.   In increments of 25 mm Hg, increase the driving pressure by clicking (+) next to the **Pressure** window, and repeat step 4 until the maximum pressure (225 mm Hg) has been reached.

6.   View your data graphically by choosing **Plot Data** from the **Tools** menu. Choose **Pressure** as the data set to be graphed, and then use the slider bars to select the pressure data to be plotted on the X-axis and the flow data to be plotted on the Y-axis. You can highlight individual data points by clicking a line in the data grid. When finished, click the close box at the top of the plot window.

How does driving pressure affect fluid flow?

_____

_____

_____

How does this plot differ from the plots for tube radius, viscosity, and tube length?

_____

_____

_____

Although changing pressure could be used as a means of blood flow control, explain why this approach would not be as effective as altering blood vessel radius.

_____

_____

_____

7.   Click **Tools** → **Print Data** to print your recorded data for this experiment. ■

Pump Mechanics

In the human body, the heart beats approximately 70 strokes each minute. Each heartbeat consists of a filling interval, during which blood moves into the chambers of the heart, and an ejection period when blood is actively pumped into the great arteries. The pumping activity of the heart can be described in terms of the phases of the cardiac cycle. Heart chambers fill during **diastole** (relaxation of the heart) and pump blood out during **systole** (contraction of the heart). As you can imagine, the length of time the heart is relaxed is one factor that determines the amount of blood within the heart at the end of the filling interval. Up to a point, increasing ventricular filling time results in a corresponding increase in ventricular volume. The volume in the ventricles at the end of diastole, just before cardiac contraction, is called the **end diastolic volume,** or **EDV.**

Blood moves from the heart into the arterial system when systolic pressure increases above the residual pressure (from the previous systole) in the great arteries leaving the heart. Although ventricular contraction causes blood ejection, the heart does not empty completely; a small quantity of blood—the **end systolic volume,** or **ESV**—remains in the ventricles at the end of systole.

Because the oxygen requirements of body tissue change depending on activity levels, we would expect the **cardiac output** (amount of blood pumped by each ventricle per minute) to vary correspondingly. We can calculate the **stroke volume** (**SV,** the amount of blood pumped per contraction of each ventricle) by subtracting the end systolic volume from the end diastolic volume (SV = EDV − ESV). We then compute cardiac output by multiplying the stroke volume by heart rate.

The human heart is a complex four-chambered organ, consisting of two individual pumps (the right and left sides) connected together in series. The right heart pumps blood through the lungs into the left heart, which in turn delivers blood to the systems of the body. Blood then returns to the right heart to complete the circuit.

Using the Pump Mechanics part of the PhysioEx program you will explore the operation of a simple one-chambered pump and apply the physical concepts in the simulation to the operation of either of the two pumps composing the human heart.

In this experiment you can vary the starting and ending volumes of the pump (analogous to EDV and ESV, respectively), driving and resistance pressures, and the diameters of the flow tubes leading to and from the pump chamber. As you proceed through the exercise, try to apply the ideas of ESV, EDV, cardiac output, stroke volume, and blood flow to the on-screen simulated pump system. For example, imagine that the flow tube leading to the pump from the left represents the pulmonary veins, while the flow tube exiting the pump to the right represents the aorta. The pump would then represent the left side of the heart.

Select **Pump Mechanics** from the **Experiment** menu. The equipment for the Pump Mechanics part of the experiment appears (Figure 5.2).

As in the previous experiment, there are two simulated electronic control units on the computer's screen. The upper apparatus is the _equipment control unit,_ which is used to adjust experiment parameters and to operate the equipment. The lower apparatus is the _data collection unit,_ in which you will record the data you accumulate.

This equipment differs slightly from that used in the Vessel Resistance experiment. There are still two beakers: the _source_ beaker on the left and the _destination_ beaker on the right. Now the pressure in each beaker is individually controlled by the small pressure units on top of the beakers. Between the two beakers is a simple pump, which can be thought of as one side of the heart, or even as a single ventricle (e.g., left ventricle). The left beaker and flow tube are analogous to the venous side of human blood flow, while arterial circulation is simulated by the right flow tube and beaker. One-way valves in the flow tubes supplying the pump ensure fluid movement in one direction—from the left beaker into the pump, and then into the right beaker. If you imagine that the pump represents the left ventricle, then think of the valve to the left of the pump as the bicuspid valve and the valve to the right of the pump as the aortic semilunar valve. The pump is driven by a pressure unit mounted on its cap. An important distinction between the pump's pressure unit and the pressure units atop the beakers is that the pump delivers pressure only during its downward stroke. Upward pump strokes are driven by pressure from the left beaker (the pump does not exert any resistance to flow from the left beaker during pump filling). In contrast, pressure in the right beaker works against the pump pressure, which means that the net pressure driving the fluid into the right beaker is calculated (automatically) by subtracting the right beaker pressure from the pump pressure. The resulting pressure difference between the pump and the right beaker is displayed in the experimental values grid in the data collection unit as **Pres.Dif.R.**

Clicking the **Auto Pump** button will cycle the pump through the number of strokes indicated in the Max. strokes window. Clicking the **Single** button cycles the pump through one stroke. During the experiment, the pump and flow rates are automatically displayed when the number of pump strokes is five or greater. The radius of each flow tube is individually controlled by clicking the appropriate button. Click (+) to increase flow tube radius or (−) to decrease flow tube radius.

The pump's stroke volume (the amount of fluid ejected in one stroke) is automatically computed by subtracting its ending volume from the starting volume. You can adjust starting and ending volumes, and thereby stroke volume, by clicking the appropriate (+) or (−) button in the equipment control unit.

The data collection unit records and displays data you accumulate during the experiments. The data set for the first experiment (**Rad.R.,** which represents right flow tube radius)

Figure 5.2 Opening screen of the Pump Mechanics experiment.

is highlighted in the **Data Sets** window. You can add or delete a data set by clicking the appropriate button to the right of the **Data Sets** window. Clicking **Delete Data Set** will erase the data set itself, including all the data it contained. The **Record Data** button at the right edge of the screen activates automatically after an experimental trial. When clicked, the **Record Data** button displays the flow rate data in the experimental values grid and saves it in the computer's memory. Clicking the **Delete Line** or **Clear Data Set** button erases any data you want to delete.

Activity 5:
Studying the Effect of Radius on Pump Activity

Although you will be manipulating the radius of only the right flow tube in this part of the exercise, try to predict the consequence of altering the left flow tube radius as you collect the experimental data. (Remember that the left flow tube simulates the pulmonary veins and the right flow tube simulates the aorta.)

1. Open the **Pump Mechanics** window if it isn't already open.

Click the **Rad.R.** data set to activate it. The data collection unit is now ready to record flow variations due to changing flow tube radius.

If the experimental values grid is not empty, click **Clear Data Set** to discard all previous values.

If the left beaker is not full, click **Refill.**

2. Adjust the **right** flow tube radius to 2.5 mm, and the **left** flow tube radius to 3.0 mm by clicking and holding the appropriate button. During the entire radius part of the experiment, maintain the other experiment conditions at:

- 40 mm Hg for left beaker pressure (this pressure drives fluid into the pump, which offers no resistance to filling)

- 120 mm Hg for pump pressure (pump pressure is the driving force that propels fluid into the right beaker)

- 80 mm Hg for right beaker pressure (this pressure is the resistance to the pump's pressure)

- 120-ml Start volume in pump (analogous to EDV)

- 50-ml End volume in pump (analogous to ESV)
- 10 strokes in the Max. strokes window

Notice that the displayed 70-ml stroke volume is automatically calculated. Before starting, click the **Single** button one or two times and watch the pump action.

To be sure you understand how this simple mechanical pump can be thought of as a simulation of the human heart, complete the following statements by circling the correct term within the parentheses:

a. When the piston is at the bottom of its travel, the volume remaining in the pump is analogous to the (EDV / ESV) of the heart.

b. The amount of fluid ejected into the right beaker by a single pump cycle is analogous to (stroke volume / cardiac output) of the heart.

c. The volume of blood in the heart just before systole is called the (EDV / ESV) and is analogous to the volume of fluid present in the simulated pump when it is at the (top / bottom) of its stroke.

3. Click the **Auto Pump** button in the equipment control unit to start the pump. After the 10 stroke volumes have been delivered, the Flow and Rate windows will automatically display the experiment results. Now click **Record Data** to display the figures you just collected in the experimental values grid. Click **Refill** to replenish the left beaker.

4. Increase the *right* flow tube radius in 0.5-mm increments, and repeat step 3 above until the maximum radius (6.0 mm) is achieved. Be sure to click **Record Data** after each trial.

5. When you have completed the experiment, view your data graphically by choosing **Plot Data** from the **Tools** menu. Choose **Rad.R.** as the data set to be graphed, and then use the slider bars to select the Rad.R. data to be plotted on the X-axis and the flow data to be plotted on the Y-axis. You can highlight individual data points by clicking a line in the data grid.

The total flow rates you just determined depend on the flow rate into the pump from the left and on the flow rate out of the pump toward the right. Consequently, the shape of the plot is different from what you might predict after viewing the vessel resistance radius graph.

Try to explain why this graph differs from the radius plot in the Vessel Resistance experiment. Remember that the flow rate into the pump did not change, whereas the flow rate out of the pump varied according to your radius manipulations.

_____

_____

_____

_____

When you have finished, click the close box at the top of the plot window.

Complete the following statements by circling the correct term within the parentheses.

a. As the right flow tube radius is increased, fluid flow rate (increases / decreases). This is analogous to (dilation / constriction) of blood vessels in the human body.

b. Even though the pump pressure remains constant, the pump rate (increases / decreases) as the radius of the right flow tube is increased. This happens because the resistance to fluid flow is (increased / decreased).

Apply your observations of the simulated mechanical pump to complete the following statements about human heart function. If you are not sure how to formulate your response, use the simulation to arrive at an answer. Circle the correct term within the parentheses.

c. The heart must contract (more / less) forcefully to maintain cardiac output if the resistance to blood flow in the vessels exiting the heart is increased.

d. Increasing the resistance (that is, constricting) the blood vessels entering the heart would (increase / decrease) the time needed to fill the heart chambers.

What do you think would happen to the flow rate and the pump rate if the left flow tube radius is changed (either increased or decreased)?

_____

_____

_____ ∎

Activity 6:
Studying the Effect of Stroke Volume on Pump Activity

Whereas the heart of a person at rest pumps about 60% of the blood in its chambers, 40% of the total amount of blood remains in the chambers after systole. The 60% of blood ejected by the heart is called the stroke volume and is the difference between EDV and ESV. Even though our simple pump in this experiment does not work exactly like the human heart, you can apply the concepts to basic cardiac function. In this experiment, you will examine how the activity of the simple pump is affected by changing the pump's starting and ending volumes.

1. Click the **Str.V.** (stroke volume) data set to activate it. If the experimental values grid is not empty, click **Clear Data Set** to discard all previous values. If the left beaker is not full, click **Refill.**

2. Adjust the stroke volume to 10 ml by setting the **Start** volume (EDV) to 120 ml and the **End** volume (ESV) to 110 ml (stroke volume = start volume − end volume). During the entire stroke volume part of the experiment, keep the other experimental conditions at:

- 40 mm Hg for left beaker pressure
- 120 mm Hg for pump pressure
- 80 mm Hg for right beaker pressure
- 3.0 mm for left and right flow tube radius
- 10 strokes in the Max. strokes window

3. Click the **Auto Pump** button to start the experiment. After 10 stroke volumes have been delivered, the Flow and Rate windows will display the experiment results given the current parameters. Click **Record Data** to display the figures you just collected in the experimental values grid. Click **Refill** to replenish the left beaker.

4. Increase the stroke volume in 10-ml increments (by decreasing the End volume) and repeat step 3 until the maximum stroke volume (120 ml) is achieved. Be sure to click the **Record Data** button after each trial. Watch the pump action during each stroke to see how you can apply the concepts of starting and ending pump volumes to EDV and ESV of the heart.

5. View your data graphically by choosing **Plot Data** from the **Tools** menu. Choose **Str.V.** as the data set to be graphed, and then use the slider bars to select the Str.V. data to be plotted on the X-axis and the pump rate data to be plotted on the Y-axis. Answer the following questions. When you have finished, click the close box at the top of the plot window.

What happened to the pump's rate as its stroke volume was increased?

_____

_____

_____

Using your simulation results as a basis for your answer, explain why an athlete's resting heart rate might be lower than that of the average person.

_____

_____

_____

Applying the simulation outcomes to the human heart, predict the effect of increasing the stroke volume on cardiac output (at any given rate).

_____

_____

_____

Circle the correct term within the parentheses: When heart rate is increased, the time of ventricular filling is (increased / decreased), which in turn (increases / decreases) the stroke volume.

What do you think might happen to the pressure in the pump during filling if the valve in the right flow tube became leaky? (Remember that the pump offers no resistance to filling.)

_____

_____

Applying this concept to the human heart, what might occur in the left heart and pulmonary blood vessels if the aortic valve became leaky?

_____

_____

What might occur if the aortic valve became slightly constricted?

_____

_____

Circle the correct term within the parentheses: In your simulation, increasing the pressure in the right beaker is analogous to the aortic valve becoming (leaky / constricted). ■

Activity 7:
Studying Combined Effects

In this section, you will set up your own experimental conditions to answer the following questions. Carefully examine each question and decide how to set experiment parameters to arrive at an answer. You can examine your previously collected data if you need additional information. Record several data points for each question as evidence for your answer (unless the question calls for a single pump stroke)

Click the **Add Data Set** button in the data collection unit. Next, create a new data set called Combined. Your newly created data set will be displayed beneath Str.V. Now click the **Combined** line to activate the data set. As you collect the supporting data for the following questions, be sure to click **Record Data** each time you have a data point you wish to keep for your records.

How is the flow rate affected when the right flow tube radius is kept constant (at 3.0 mm) and the left flow tube radius is modified (either up or down)?

_____

_____

_____

_____

How does decreasing left flow tube radius affect pump chamber filling time? Does it affect pump chamber emptying?

_____

_____

_____

You have already examined the effect of changing the pump's end volume as a way of manipulating stroke volume. What happens to flow and pump rate when you keep the end volume constant and alter the start volume to manipulate stroke volume?

_____

_____

_____

_____

Try manipulating the pressure delivered to the left beaker. How does changing the left beaker pressure affect flow rate? (This change would be similar to changing pulmonary vein pressure.)

_____

_____

If the left beaker pressure is decreased to 10 mm Hg, how is pump-filling time affected?

_____

_____

_____

What happens to the pump rate if the filling time is shortened?

_____

_____

What happens to fluid flow when the right beaker pressure equals the pump pressure?

_____

_____

_____ ■

Activity 8:
Studying Compensation

In this activity you will explore the concept of cardiovascular compensation. Click the **Add Data Set** button in the data collection unit. Next, create a new data set called **Comp.** Your newly created data set will be displayed beneath Combined.

Now click the **Comp.** line to activate the data set. As you collect the supporting data for the following questions, be sure to click **Record Data** each time you have a data point you wish to keep for your records.

Adjust the experimental conditions to the following:

- 40 mm Hg for left beaker pressure
- 120 mm Hg for pump pressure
- 80 mm Hg for right beaker pressure
- 3.0 mm for left and right flow tube radius
- 10 strokes in the Max. strokes window
- 120-ml Start volume in pump
- 50-ml End volume in pump

Click **Auto Pump,** and then record your flow rate data. Let's declare the value you just obtained to be the "normal" flow rate for the purpose of this exercise.

Now decrease the right flow tube radius to 2.5 mm, and run another trial. How does this flow rate compare with "normal"?

_____

_____

Leave the right flow tube radius at 2.5 mm radius, and try to adjust one or more other conditions to return flow to "normal." Think logically about what condition(s) might compensate for a decrease in flow tube radius. How were you able to accomplish this? (Hint: There are several ways.)

_____

_____

_____

Circle the correct term within the parentheses: Decreasing the right flow tube radius is similar to a partial (leakage / blockage) of the aortic valve or (increased / decreased) resistance in the arterial system.

Explain how the human heart might compensate for such a condition.

_____

_____

_____

_____

To increase (or decrease) blood flow to a particular body system (e.g., digestive), would it be better to adjust heart rate or blood vessel diameter? Explain.

_____

_____

_____

_____

Complete the following statements by circling the correct response. (If necessary, use the pump simulation to help you with your answers.)

a. If we decreased overall peripheral resistance in the human body (as in an athlete), the heart would need to generate (more / less) pressure to deliver an adequate amount of blood flow, and arterial pressure would be (higher / lower).

b. If the diameter of the arteries of the body were partly filled with fatty deposits, the heart would need to generate (more / less) force to maintain blood flow, and pressure in the arterial system would be (higher / lower) than normal.

Click **Tools** → **Print Data** to print your recorded data for this experiment. ■

Histology Review Supplement

Turn to page 128 for a review of cardiovascular tissue.

Frog Cardiovascular Physiology

Objectives

1. To list the properties of cardiac muscle as automaticity and rhythmicity, and to define each.

2. To explain the statement, "Cardiac muscle has an intrinsic ability to beat."

3. To compare the relative length of the refractory period of cardiac muscle with that of skeletal muscle, and to explain why it is not possible to tetanize cardiac muscle.

4. To define *extrasystole,* and to explain at what point in the cardiac cycle (and on an ECG tracing) an extrasystole can be induced.

5. To describe the effect of the following on heart rate: vagal stimulation, cold, heat, pilocarpine, atropine, epinephrine, digitalis, and potassium, sodium, and calcium ions.

6. To define *vagal escape* and discuss its value.

7. To define *ectopic pacemaker.*

Investigation of human cardiovascular physiology is very interesting, but many areas obviously do not lend themselves to experimentation. It would be tantamount to murder to inject a human subject with various drugs to observe their effects on heart activity or to expose the human heart in order to study the length of its refractory period. However, this type of investigation can be done on frogs or computer simulations and provides valuable data because the physiological mechanisms in these animals, or programmed into the computer simulation, are similar if not identical to those in humans.

In this exercise, you will conduct the cardiac investigations just mentioned.

Special Electrical Properties of Cardiac Muscle: Automaticity and Rhythmicity

Cardiac muscle differs from skeletal muscle both functionally and in its fine structure. Skeletal muscle must be electrically stimulated to contract. In contrast, heart muscle can and does depolarize spontaneously in the absence of external stimulation. This property, called **automaticity,** is due to plasma membranes that have reduced permeability to potassium ions but still allow sodium ions to slowly leak into the cells. This leakage causes the muscle cells to slowly depolarize until the action potential threshold is reached and *fast calcium channels* open, allowing Ca^{2+} entry from the extracellular fluid. Shortly thereafter, contraction occurs.

The spontaneous depolarization-repolarization events occur in a regular and continuous manner in cardiac muscle, a property referred to as **rhythmicity.**

In the following experiment, you will observe these properties of cardiac muscle in a computer simulation. Additionally, your instructor may demonstrate this procedure using a real frog.

Nervous Stimulation of the Heart

Both the parasympathetic and sympathetic nervous systems innervate the heart. Stimulation of the sympathetic nervous system increases the rate and force of contraction of the heart. Stimulation of the parasympathetic nervous system (vagal nerves) decreases the depolarization rhythm of the sinoatrial node and slows transmission of excitation through the atrioventricular node. If vagal stimulation is excessive, the heart will stop beating. After a short time, the ventricles will begin to beat again. This is referred to as **vagal escape** and may be the result of sympathetic reflexes or initiation of a rhythm by the Purkinje fibers.

Baseline Frog Heart Activity

The heart's effectiveness as a pump is dependent both on intrinsic (within the heart) and extrinsic (external to the heart) controls. In the first experimental series, Activities 1–3, you will investigate some of these factors.

The nodal system, in which the "pacemaker" imposes its depolarization rate on the rest of the heart, is one intrinsic factor that influences the heart's pumping action. If its impulses fail to reach the ventricles (as in heart block), the ventricles continue to beat but at their own inherent rate, which is much slower than that usually imposed on them. Although heart contraction does not depend on nerve impulses, its rate can be modified by extrinsic impulses reaching it through the

autonomic nerves. Cardiac activity is also modified by various chemicals, hormones, ions, and metabolites. The effects of several of these chemical factors are examined in the next experimental series, Activities 4–9.

The frog heart has two atria and a single, incompletely divided ventricle. The pacemaker is located in the sinus venosus, an enlarged region between the venae cavae and the right atrium. The sinoatrial (SA) node of mammals may have evolved from the sinus venosus.

Choose **Frog Cardiovascular Physiology** from the main menu. The opening screen will appear in a few seconds (Figure 6.1). When the program starts, you will see a tracing of the frog's heartbeat on the *oscilloscope display* in the upper right part of the screen. Because the simulation automatically adjusts itself to your computer's speed, you may not see the heart tracing appear in real time. If you want to increase the speed of the tracing (at the expense of tracing quality), click the **Tools** menu, choose **Modify Display,** and then select **Increase Speed.**

The oscilloscope display shows the ventricular contraction rate in the Heart Rate window. The *heart activity window*

Figure 6.1   Opening screen of the Electrical Stimulation experiment.

to the right of the Heart Rate display provides the following messages:

- Heart Rate Normal—displayed when the heart is beating under resting conditions.

- Heart Rate Changing—displayed when the heart rate is increasing or decreasing.

- Heart Rate Stable—displayed when the heart rate is steady, but higher or lower than normal. For example, if you applied a chemical that increased heart rate to a stable but higher-than-normal rate, you would see this message.

The *electrical stimulator* is below the oscilloscope display. In the experiment, clicking **Single Stimulus** delivers a single electrical shock to the frog heart. Clicking **Multiple Stimulus** delivers repeated electrical shocks at the rate indicated in the Stimuli/sec window just below the Multiple Stimulus button. When the **Multiple Stimulus** button is clicked, it changes to a **Stop Stimulus** button that allows you to stop electrical stimulation as desired. Clicking the (+) or (−) buttons next to the Stimuli/sec window adjusts the stimulus rate. The voltage delivered when Single Stimulus or Multiple Stimulus is clicked is displayed in the **Voltage** window just below the Single Stimulus button. The simulation automatically adjusts the voltage for the experiment. The postlike apparatus extending upward from the electrical stimulator is the *electrode holder* into which you will drag-and-drop electrodes from the supply cabinet in the bottom left corner of the screen.

The left side of the screen contains the apparatus that sustains the frog heart. The heart has been lifted away from the body of the frog by a hook passed through the apex of the heart. Although the frog cannot be seen because it is in the dissection tray, its heart has not been removed from its circulatory system. A thin string connects the hook in the heart to the force transducer at the top of the support bracket. As the heart contracts, the string exerts tension on the force transducer that converts the contraction into the oscilloscope tracing. The slender white strand extending from the heart toward the right side of the dissection tray is the vagus nerve. In the simulation, room-temperature (23°C) frog Ringer's solution continuously drips onto the heart to keep it moist and responsive so that a regular heart beat is maintained.

The two *electrodes* you will use during the experiment are located in the supply cabinet beneath the dissection tray. The **Direct Heart Stimulation** electrode is used to stimulate the ventricular muscle directly. The **Vagus Nerve Stimulation** electrode is used to stimulate the vagus nerve. To position either electrode, click and drag the electrode to the two-pronged plug in the electrode holder and then release the mouse button.

Activity 1:
Recording Baseline Frog Heart Activity

1. Before beginning to stimulate the frog heart experimentally, watch several heartbeats. Be sure you can distinguish atrial and ventricular contraction (Figure 6.2a).

2. Record the number of ventricular contractions per minute displayed in the Heart Rate window under the oscilloscope.

_____ bpm (beats per minute) ■

Activity 2:
Investigating the Refractory Period of Cardiac Muscle

In Exercise 2 you saw that repeated rapid stimuli could cause skeletal muscle to remain in a contracted state. In other words, the muscle could be tetanized. This was possible because of the relatively short refractory period of skeletal muscle. In this experiment you will investigate the refractory period of cardiac muscle and its response to stimulation.

1. Click and hold the mouse button on the **Direct Heart Stimulation** electrode, and drag it to the electrode holder.

2. Release the mouse button to lock the electrode in place. The electrode will touch the ventricular muscle tissue.

3. Deliver single shocks by clicking **Single Stimulus** at each of the following times. You may need to practice to acquire the correct technique.

- near the beginning of ventricular contraction

- at the peak of ventricular contraction

- during the relaxation part of the cycle

Watch for **extrasystoles,** which are extra beats that show up riding on the ventricular contraction peak. Also note the compensatory pause, which allows the heart to get back on schedule after an extrasystole (Figure 6.2b).

(a) One-second time line

(b) One-second time line

Figure 6.2 Recording of contractile activity of a frog heart. (a) Normal heartbeat. **(b)** Induction of an extrasystole.

During which portion of the cardiac cycle was it possible to induce an extrasystole?

_____

_____

4.   Attempt to tetanize the heart by clicking **Multiple Stimulus.** Electrical shocks will be delivered to the muscle at a rate of 20 stimuli/sec. What is the result?

_____

_____

Considering the function of the heart, why is it important that the heart muscle cannot be tetanized?

_____

_____

5.   Click **Stop Stimulus** to stop the electrical stimulation. ∎

Activity 3:
Examining the Effect of Vagus Nerve Stimulation

The vagus nerve carries parasympathetic impulses to the heart, which modify heart activity.

1.   Click the **Direct Heart Stimulation** electrode to return it to the supply cabinet.

2.   Click and drag the **Vagus Nerve Stimulation** electrode to the electrode holder.

3.   Release the mouse button to lock the electrode in place. The vagus nerve will automatically be draped over the electrode contacts.

4.   Adjust the stimulator to 50 stimuli/sec by clicking the (+) or (−) buttons.

5.   Click **Multiple Stimulus.** Allow the vagal stimulation to continue until the heart stops momentarily and then begins to beat again (vagal escape), and then click **Stop Stimulus.**

What is the effect of vagal stimulation on heart rate?

_____

_____

The phenomenon of vagal escape demonstrates that many factors are involved in heart regulation and that any deleterious factor (in this case, excessive vagal stimulation) will be overcome, if possible, by other physiological mechanisms such as activation of the sympathetic division of the autonomic nervous system (ANS). ∎

Assessing Physical and Chemical Modifiers of Heart Rate

Now that you have observed normal frog heart activity, you will have an opportunity to investigate the effects of various modifying factors on heart activity. After removing the agent in each activity, allow the heart to return to its normal rate before continuing with the testing.

Choose **Modifiers of Heart Rate** from the **Experiment** menu. The opening screen will appear in a few seconds (Figure 6.3). The appearance and functionality of the *oscilloscope display* is the same as it was in the Electrical Stimulation experiment. The *solutions shelf* above the oscilloscope display contains the chemicals you'll use to modify heart rate in the experiment. You can choose the temperature of the Ringer's solution dispensed by clicking the appropriate button in the Ringer's dispenser at the left part of the screen. The doors to the supply cabinet are closed during this experiment because the electrical stimulator is not used.

When you click **Record Data** in the *data control unit* below the oscilloscope, your data is stored in the computer's memory and is displayed in the data grid at the bottom of the screen; data displayed include the solution used and the resulting heart rate. If you are not satisfied with a trial, you can click **Delete Line.** Click **Clear Table** if you wish to repeat the entire experiment.

Activity 4:
Assessing the Effect of Temperature

1.   Click the **5°C Ringer's** button to bathe the frog heart in cold Ringer's solution. Watch the recording for a change in cardiac activity.

2.   When the heart activity window displays the message Heart Rate Stable, click **Record Data** to retain your data in the data grid.

What change occurred with the cold (5°C) Ringer's solution?

_____

3.   Now click the **23°C Ringer's** button to flood the heart with fresh room-temperature Ringer's solution.

4.   After you see the message Heart Rate Normal in the heart activity window, click the **32°C Ringer's** button.

5.   When the heart activity window displays the message Heart Rate Stable, click **Record Data** to retain your data.

What change occurred with the warm (32°C) Ringer's solution?

_____

Record the heart rate at the two temperatures below.

_____ bpm at 5°C; _____ bpm at 32°C

Figure 6.3 **Opening screen of the Modifiers of Heart Rate experiment.**

What can you say about the effect of temperature on heart rate?

_____

_____

6.   Click the **23°C Ringer's** button to flush the heart with fresh Ringer's solution. Watch the heart activity window for the message Heart Rate Normal before beginning the next test. ∎

Activity 5:
Assessing the Effect of Pilocarpine

1.   Click and hold the mouse on the **pilocarpine** dropper cap.

2.   Drag the dropper cap to a point about an inch above the heart, and release the mouse.

3.   Pilocarpine solution will be dispensed onto the heart, and the dropper cap will automatically return to the pilocarpine bottle.

4.   Watch the heart activity window for the message Heart Rate Stable, indicating that the heart rate has stabilized under the effects of pilocarpine.

5.   After the heart rate stabilizes, record the heart rate in the space provided below, and click **Record Data** to retain your data in the grid.

_____ bpm

What happened when the heart was bathed in the pilocarpine solution?

_____

6.   Click the **23°C Ringer's** button to flush the heart with fresh Ringer's solution. Watch the heart activity window for

the message Heart Rate Normal, an indication that the heart is ready for the next test. ■

Pilocarpine simulates the effect of parasympathetic nerve (hence, vagal) stimulation by enhancing acetylcholine release; such drugs are called parasympathomimetic drugs.

Activity 6:
Assessing the Effect of Atropine

1. Drag-and-drop the **atropine** dropper cap to a point about an inch above the heart.

2. Atropine solution will automatically drip onto the heart, and the dropper cap will return to its position in the atropine bottle.

3. Watch the heart activity window for the message Heart Rate Stable.

4. After the heart rate stabilizes, record the heart rate in the space below, and click **Record Data** to retain your data in the grid.

_____ bpm

What is the effect of atropine on the heart?

_____

Atropine is a drug that blocks the effect of the neurotransmitter acetylcholine, liberated by the parasympathetic nerve endings. Do your results accurately reflect this effect of atropine?

_____

Are pilocarpine and atropine agonists or antagonists in their effects on heart activity?

_____

5. Click the **23°C Ringer's** button to flush the heart with fresh Ringer's solution. Watch the heart activity window for the message Heart Rate Normal before beginning the next test. ■

Activity 7:
Assessing the Effect of Epinephrine

1. Drag-and-drop the **epinephrine** dropper cap to a point about an inch above the heart.

2. Epinephrine solution will be dispensed onto the heart, and the dropper cap will return to the epinephrine bottle.

3. Watch the heart activity window for the message Heart Rate Stable.

4. After the heart rate stabilizes, record the heart rate in the space provided below, and click **Record Data** to retain your data in the grid.

_____ bpm

What happened when the heart was bathed in the epinephrine solution?

_____

Which division of the autonomic nervous system does its effect imitate?

_____

5. Click the **23°C Ringer's** button to flush the heart with fresh Ringer's solution. Watch the heart activity window for the message Heart Rate Normal, meaning that the heart is ready for the next test. ■

Activity 8:
Assessing the Effect of Digitalis

1. Drag-and-drop the **digitalis** dropper cap to a point about an inch above the heart.

2. Digitalis solution will automatically drip onto the heart, and then the dropper will return to the digitalis bottle.

3. Watch the heart activity window to the right of the Heart Rate window for the message Heart Rate Stable.

4. After the heart rate stabilizes, record the heart rate in the space provided below, and click **Record Data** to retain your data in the grid.

_____ bpm

What is the effect of digitalis on the heart?

_____

5. Click the **23°C Ringer's** button to flush the heart with fresh Ringer's solution. Watch the heart activity window for the message Heart Rate Normal, then proceed to the next test. ■

Digitalis is a drug commonly prescribed for heart patients with congestive heart failure. It slows heart rate, providing more time for venous return and decreasing the workload on the weakened heart. These effects are thought to be due to inhibition of the sodium-potassium pump and enhancement of Ca^{2+} entry into myocardial fibers.

Activity 9:
Assessing the Effect of Various Ions

To test the effect of various ions on the heart, apply the desired solution using the following method.

1. Drag-and-drop the **calcium ions** dropper cap to a point about an inch above the heart.

2. Calcium ions will automatically be dripped onto the heart, and the dropper cap will return to the calcium ions bottle.

3. Watch the heart activity window for the message Heart Rate Stable.

4. After the heart rate stabilizes, record the heart rate in the space provided below, and click **Record Data** to retain your data in the grid.

5. Click the **23°C Ringer's** button to flush the heart with fresh Ringer's solution. Watch the heart activity window for the message Heart Rate Normal, which means that the heart is ready for the next test.

6. Repeat steps 1 through 5 for **sodium ions** and then **potassium ions.**

Effect of Ca^{2+}:

Does the heart rate stabilize and remain stable?

_____

Describe your observations of force and rhythm of the heart-beat.

_____

_____

Effect of Na^+:

Does the heart rate stabilize and remain stable?

_____

Describe your observations of force and rhythm of the heart-beat.

_____

_____

Effect of K^+:

Does the heart rate stabilize and remain stable?

_____

Describe your observations of force and rhythm of the heart-beat.

_____

_____

Potassium ion concentration is normally higher within cells than in the extracellular fluid. _Hyperkalemia_ decreases the resting potential of plasma membranes, thus decreasing the force of heart contraction. In some cases, the conduction rate of the heart is so depressed that **ectopic pacemakers** (pacemakers appearing erratically and at abnormal sites in the heart muscle) appear in the ventricle, and fibrillation may occur.

Was there any evidence of premature beats in the recording of potassium ion effects?

_____

Was arrhythmia produced with any of the ions tested?

_____ If so, which? _____

7. Click **Tools → Print Data** to print your recorded data for this experiment. ■

Histology Review Supplement

Turn to page 128 for a review of cardiovascular tissue.

Respiratory System Mechanics

T he two phases of **pulmonary ventilation** or **breathing** are **inspiration,** during which air is taken into the lungs, and **expiration,** during which air is expelled from the lungs. Inspiration occurs as the external intercostal muscles and the diaphragm contract. The diaphragm, normally a dome-shaped muscle, flattens as it moves inferiorly while the external intercostal muscles between the ribs lift the rib cage. These cooperative actions increase the thoracic volume. Because the increase in thoracic volume causes a partial vacuum, air rushes into the lungs. During normal expiration, the inspiratory muscles relax, causing the diaphragm to rise and the chest wall to move inward. The thorax returns to its normal shape due to the elastic properties of the lung and thoracic wall. Like a deflating balloon, the pressure in the lungs rises, which forces air out of the lungs and airways. Although expiration is normally a passive process, abdominal wall muscles and the internal intercostal muscles can contract to force air from the lungs. Blowing up a balloon is an example where such **forced expiration** would occur.

Simulating Spirometry: Measuring Respiratory Volumes and Capacities

This computerized simulation allows you to investigate the basic mechanical function of the respiratory system as you determine lung volumes and capacities. The concepts you will learn by studying this simulated mechanical lung can then be applied to help you understand the operation of the human respiratory system.

Normal quiet breathing moves about 500 ml (0.5 liter) of air (the tidal volume) in and out of the lungs with each breath, but this amount can vary due to a person's size, sex, age, physical condition, and immediate respiratory needs. The terms used for the normal respiratory volumes are defined next. The values are for the normal adult male and are approximate.

Normal Respiratory Volumes

Tidal volume (TV): Amount of air inhaled or exhaled with each breath under resting conditions (500 ml)

Expiratory reserve volume (ERV): Amount of air that can be forcefully exhaled after a normal tidal volume exhalation (1200 ml)

Inspiratory reserve volume (IRV): Amount of air that can be forcefully inhaled after a normal tidal volume inhalation (3100 ml)

Objectives

1. To define the following terms:

   ventilation, inspiration, expiration, forced expiration, tidal volume, expiratory reserve volume, inspiratory reserve volume, residual volume, vital capacity, forced expiratory volume, minute respiratory volume, surfactant, and *pneumothorax.*

2. To describe the role of muscles and volume changes in the mechanics of breathing.

3. To understand that the lungs do not contain muscle and that respirations are therefore caused by external forces.

4. To explore the effect of changing airway resistance on breathing.

5. To study the effect of surfactant on lung function.

6. To examine the factors that cause lung collapse.

7. To understand the effects of hyperventilation, rebreathing, and breath holding on the CO_2 level in the blood.

Residual volume (RV): Amount of air remaining in the lungs after complete exhalation (1200 ml)

Vital capacity (VC): Maximum amount of air that can be exhaled after a normal maximal inspiration (4800 ml)

$$VC = TV + IRV + ERV$$

Total lung capacity (TLC): Sum of vital capacity and residual volume

Pulmonary Function Tests

Forced vital capacity (FVC): Amount of air that can be expelled when the subject takes the deepest possible breath and exhales as completely and rapidly as possible

Forced expiratory volume (FEV$_1$): Measures the percentage of the vital capacity that is exhaled during 1 second of the FVC test (normally 75% to 85% of the vital capacity)

Choose **Respiratory System Mechanics** from the main menu. The opening screen for the Respiratory Volumes experiment will appear in a few seconds (Figure 7.1). The main features on the screen when the program starts are a pair of *simulated lungs within a bell jar* at the left side of the screen, an *oscilloscope* at the upper right part of the screen, a *data display* area beneath the oscilloscope, and a *data control unit* at the bottom of the screen.

The black rubber "diaphragm" sealing the bottom of the glass bell jar is attached to a rod in the pump just below the jar. The rod moves the rubber diaphragm up and down to change the pressure within the bell jar (comparable to the intrapleural pressure in the body). As the diaphragm moves inferiorly, the resulting volume increase creates a partial vacuum in the bell jar because of lowered pressure. This partial vacuum causes air to be sucked into the tube at the top of the bell jar and then into the simulated lungs.

Conversely, as the diaphragm moves up, the rising pressure within the bell jar forces air out of the lungs. The partition between the two lungs compartmentalizes the bell jar into right and left sides. The lungs are connected to an air-flow

Figure 7.1 Opening screen of the Respiratory Volumes experiment.

tube in which the diameter is adjustable by clicking the (+) and (−) buttons next to the Radius window in the equipment atop the bell jar. The volume of each breath that passes through the single air-flow tube above the bell jar is displayed in the Flow window. Clicking **Start** below the bell jar begins a trial run in which the simulated lungs will "breathe" in normal tidal volumes and the oscilloscope will display the tidal tracing. When **ERV** is clicked, the lungs will exhale maximally at the bottom of a tidal stroke and the expiratory reserve volume will be displayed in the Exp. Res. Vol. window below the oscilloscope. When **FVC** is clicked, the lungs will first inhale maximally and then exhale fully to demonstrate forced vital capacity. After ERV and FVC have been measured, the remaining lung values will be calculated and displayed in the small windows below the oscilloscope.

The data control equipment in the lower part of the screen records and displays data accumulated during the experiments. When you click **Record Data,** your data is recorded in the computer's memory and is displayed in the data grid. Data displayed in the data grid include the Radius, Flow, TV (tidal volume), ERV (expiratory reserve volume), IRV (inspiratory reserve volume), RV (residual volume), VC (vital capacity), FEV_1 (forced expiratory volume—1 second), TLC (total lung capacity), and Pump Rate. Clicking **Delete Line** allows you to discard the data for a single run; clicking **Clear Table** erases the entire experiment to allow you to start over.

If you need help identifying any piece of equipment, choose **Balloons On** from the **Help** menu, and move the mouse pointer onto any piece of equipment visible on the computer's screen. As the pointer touches the object, a pop-up window will identify the equipment. To close the pop-up window, move the mouse pointer away from the equipment. Choose **Balloons Off** to turn off this help feature.

Activity 1:
Measuring Respiratory Volumes

Your first experiment will establish the baseline respiratory values.

1. If the grid in the data control unit is not empty, click **Clear Table** to discard all previous data.

2. Adjust the radius of the airways to 5.00 mm by clicking the appropriate button next to the Radius window.

3. Click **Start,** and allow the tracing to complete. Watch the simulated lungs begin to breathe as a result of the "contraction and relaxation" of the diaphragm. Simultaneously, the oscilloscope will display a tracing of the tidal volume for each breath. The Flow window atop the bell jar indicates the tidal volume for each breath, and the Tidal Vol. window below the oscilloscope shows the average tidal volume. The Pump Rate window displays the number of breaths per minute.

4. Click **Clear Tracings.**

5. Now click **Start** again. After a second or two, click **ERV,** wait 2 seconds and then click **FVC** to complete the measurement of respiratory volumes. The expiratory reserve volume, inspiratory reserve volume, and residual volume will be auto-

matically calculated and displayed from the tests you have performed so far. Also, the equipment calculates and displays the total lung capacity.

6. Compute the **minute respiratory volume (MRV)** using the following formula (you can use the **Calculator** in the **Tools** menu):

$$MRV = TV \times BPM \text{ (breaths per minute)}$$

MRV _____ ml/min

7. Does expiratory reserve volume include tidal volume?

_____ Explain your answer. _____

_____

_____

8. Now click **Record Data** to record the current experimental data in the data grid. Then click **Clear Tracings.**

9. If you want to print a tracing at any time, click **Tools** and then **Print Graph.** ∎

Activity 2:
Examining the Effect of Changing Airway Resistance on Respiratory Volumes

Lung diseases are often classified as obstructive or restrictive. With an obstructive problem, expiratory flow is affected, whereas a restrictive problem might indicate reduced inspiratory volume. Although they are not diagnostic, pulmonary function tests such as FEV_1 can help a clinician determine the difference between obstructive and restrictive problems. FEV_1 is the forced volume exhaled in one second. In obstructive disorders like chronic bronchitis and asthma, airway resistance is increased and FEV_1 will be low. Here you will explore the effect of changing the diameter of the airway on pulmonary function.

1. Do *not* clear the data table from the previous experiment.

2. Adjust the radius of the airways to 4.50 mm by clicking the (−) button next to the Radius window.

3. Click **Start** to begin respirations.

4. Click **FVC.** As you saw in the previous test, the simulated lungs will inhale maximally and then exhale as forcefully as possible. FEV_1 will be displayed in the FEV_1 window below the oscilloscope.

5. When the lungs stop respiring, click **Record Data** to record the current data in the data grid.

6. Decrease the radius of the airways in 0.50-mm decrements and repeat steps 4 and 5 until the minimum radius (3.00 mm) is achieved. Be sure to click **Record Data** after each trial. Click **Clear Tracings** between trials. If you make an error and want to delete a single value, click the data line in the data grid and then click **Delete Line.**

7. A useful way to express FEV_1 is as a percentage of the forced vital capacity. Copy the FEV_1 and vital capacity values from the computer screen to the chart below, and then calculate the FEV_1 (%) by dividing the FEV_1 volume by the vital capacity volume and multiply by 100. Record the FEV_1 (%) in Chart 1 at the bottom of this page. You can use the **Calculator** under the **Tools** menu.

_____

Explain your answer. _____

_____

_____

8. Click **Tools → Print Data** to print your data. ■

Simulating Factors Affecting Respirations

This part of the computer simulation allows you to explore the action of surfactant on pulmonary function and the effect of changing the intrapleural pressure.

Choose **Factors Affecting Respirations** from the **Experiment** menu. The opening screen will appear in a few seconds (Figure 7.2). The basic features on the screen when the program starts are the same as in the Respiratory Volumes experiment screen. Additional equipment includes a surfactant dispenser atop the bell jar and valves on each side of the bell jar. Each time **Surfactant** is clicked, a measured amount of surfactant is sprayed into the lungs. Clicking **Flush** washes surfactant from the lungs to prepare for another run.

Clicking the valve button (which currently reads **valve closed**) allows the pressure within that side of the bell jar to equalize with the atmospheric pressure. When **Reset** is clicked, the lungs are prepared for another run.

Data accumulated during a run are displayed in the windows below the oscilloscope. When you click **Record Data,**

that data is recorded in the computer's memory and is displayed in the data grid. Data displayed in the data grid include the Radius, Pump Rate, the amount of Surfactant, Pressure Left (pressure in the left lung), Pressure Right (pressure in the right lung), Flow Left (air flow in the left lung), Flow Right (air flow in the right lung), and Total Flow. Clicking **Delete Line** allows you to discard data values for a single run, and clicking **Clear Table** erases the entire experiment to allow you to start over.

Activity 3:
Examining the Effect of Surfactant

At any gas-liquid boundary, the molecules of the liquid are attracted more strongly to each other than they are to the air molecules. This unequal attraction produces tension at the liquid surface called *surface tension.* Because surface tension resists any force that tends to increase surface area, it acts to decrease the size of hollow spaces, such as the alveoli or microscopic air spaces within the lungs. If the film lining the air spaces in the lung were pure water, it would be very difficult, if not impossible, to inflate the lungs. However, the aqueous film covering the alveolar surfaces contains **surfactant,** a detergent-like lipoprotein that decreases surface tension by reducing the attraction of water molecules for each other. You will explore the action of surfactant in this experiment.

1. If the data grid is not empty, click **Clear Table** to discard all previous data values.

2. Adjust the airway radius to 5.00 mm by clicking the appropriate button next to the Radius window.

3. If necessary, click **Flush** to clear the simulated lungs of existing surfactant.

4. Click **Start,** and allow a baseline run without added surfactant to complete.

5. When the run completes, click **Record Data.**

6. Now click **Surfactant** twice.

7. Click **Start** to begin the surfactant run.

8. When the lungs stop respiring, click **Record Data** to display the data in the grid.

Chart 1	FEV1 as % of VC		
Radius	**FEV₁**	**Vital Capacity**	**FEV₁ (%)**
5.00			
4.50			
4.00			
3.50			
3.00			

Figure 7.2 **Opening screen of the Factors Affecting Respirations experiment.**

What happened to the FEV_1 (%) as the radius of the airways was decreased?_____

_____

How has the air flow changed compared to the baseline run?

_____

_____

Premature infants often have difficulty breathing. Explain why this might be so. (Use your text as needed.)

_____

_____ ■

Activity 4:
Investigating Intrapleural Pressure

The pressure within the pleural cavity, **intrapleural pressure,** is less than the pressure within the alveoli. This negative

pressure condition is caused by two forces, the tendency of the lung to recoil due to its elastic properties and the surface tension of the alveolar fluid. These two forces act to pull the lungs away from the thoracic wall, creating a partial vacuum in the pleural cavity. Because the pressure in the intrapleural space is lower than atmospheric pressure, any opening created in the thoracic wall equalizes the intrapleural pressure with the atmospheric pressure by allowing air to enter the pleural cavity, a condition called **pneumothorax.** Pneumothorax allows lung collapse, a condition called **atelectasis** (at″ĕ-lik′tah-sis).

In the simulated respiratory system on the computer's screen, the intrapleural space is the space between the wall of the bell jar and the outer wall of the lung it contains. The pressure difference between inspiration and expiration for the left lung and for the right lung is individually displayed in the Pressure Left and Pressure Right windows below the oscilloscope.

1. Do *not* discard your previous data.

2. Click **Clear Tracings** to clean up the screen, and then click **Flush** to clear the lungs of surfactant from the previous run.

3.   Adjust the radius of the airways to 5.00 mm by clicking the appropriate button next to the Radius window.

4.   Click **Start,** and allow one screen of respirations to complete. Notice the negative pressure condition displayed below the oscilloscope when the lungs inhale.

5.   When the lungs stop respiring, click **Record Data** to display the data in the grid.

6.   Now click the valve button (which currently reads **valve closed**) on the left side of the bell jar above the Start button to open the valve.

7.   Click **Start** to begin the run.

8.   When the run completes, click **Record Data** again.

What happened to the lung in the left side of the bell jar?

_____

_____

_____

How did the pressure in the left lung differ from that in the right lung?

_____

_____

Explain your reasoning. _____

_____

_____

How did the total air flow in this trial compare with that in the previous trial in which the pleural cavities were intact?

_____

_____

What do you think would happen if the two lungs were in a single large cavity instead of separate cavities?

_____

_____

9.   Now close the valve you opened earlier by clicking it again, and then click **Start** to begin a new trial.

10.   When the run completes, click **Record Data** to display the data in the grid.

Did the deflated lung reinflate? _____

Explain your answer. _____

_____

_____

11.   Click the **Reset** button atop the bell jar. This action draws the air out of the intrapleural space and returns it to normal resting condition.

12.   Click **Start,** and allow the run to complete.

13.   When the run completes, click **Record Data** to display the data in the grid.

14.   Click **Tools → Print Data** to print data.

Why did lung function in the deflated (left) lung return to normal after you clicked Reset?

_____

_____   ■

Simulating Variations in Breathing

This part of the computer simulation allows you to examine the effects of hyperventilation, rebreathing, and breath holding on CO_2 level in the blood.

Choose **Variations in Breathing** from the **Experiment** menu. The opening screen will appear in a few seconds (Figure 7.3). The basic features on the screen when the program starts are the same as in the lung volumes screen. The buttons beneath the oscilloscope control the various possible breathing patterns. Clicking **Rapid Breathing** causes the lungs to breathe faster than normal. A small bag automatically covers the airway tube when **Rebreathing** is clicked. Clicking **Breath Holding** causes the lungs to stop respiring. Click **Normal Breathing** at any time to resume normal tidal cycles. The window next to the Start button displays the breathing pattern being performed by the simulated lungs.

The windows below the oscilloscope display the P_{CO_2} (partial pressure of CO_2) of the air in the lungs, Maximum P_{CO_2}, Minimum P_{CO_2}, and Pump rate.

Data accumulated during a run are displayed in the windows below the oscilloscope. When you click **Record Data,** that data is recorded in the computer's memory and is displayed in the data grid. Data displayed in the data grid include the condition, P_{CO_2}, maximum P_{CO_2}, minimum P_{CO_2}, pump rate, radius, and total flow. Clicking **Delete Line** allows you to discard data values for a single run, and clicking **Clear Table** erases the entire experiment to allow you to start over.

Activity 5:
Exploring Various Breathing Patterns

You will establish the baseline respiratory values in this first experiment.

1.   If the grid in the data control unit is not empty, click **Clear Table** to discard all previous data.

2.   Adjust the radius of the airways to 5.00 mm by clicking the appropriate button next to the Radius window. Now, read through steps 3–5 before attempting to execute them.

Figure 7.3 Opening screen of the Variations in Breathing experiment.

3. Click **Start,** and notice that it changes to **Stop** to allow you to stop the respiration. Watch the simulated lungs begin to breathe as a result of the external mechanical forces supplied by the pump below the bell jar. Simultaneously, the oscilloscope will display a tracing of the tidal volume for each breath.

4. After 2 seconds, click the **Rapid Breathing** button and watch the P_{CO_2} displays. The breathing pattern will change to short, rapid breaths. The P_{CO_2} of the air in the lungs will be displayed in the small window to the right of the Rapid Breathing button.

5. Watch the oscilloscope display and the P_{CO_2} window, and click **Stop** before the tracing reaches the end of the screen.

What happens to P_{CO_2} during rapid breathing? Explain your answer.

6. Click **Record Data.**

7. Now click **Clear Tracings** to prepare for the next run.

Rebreathing

When **Rebreathing** is clicked, a small bag will appear over the end of the air tube to allow the air within the lungs to be repeatedly inspired and expired.

1. Click **Start,** wait 2 seconds, and then click **Rebreathing.**

2. Watch the breathing pattern on the oscilloscope, and notice the P_{CO_2} during the course of the run. Click **Stop** when the tracing reaches the right edge of the oscilloscope.

What happens to P_{CO_2} during the entire time of the rebreathing activity?

Did the depth of the breathing pattern change during rebreathing? (Carefully examine the tracing for rate and depth changes; the changes can be subtle.) Explain your observations.

_____

_____

_____

_____

3. Click **Record Data,** and then click **Clear Tracings** to prepare for the next run.

Breath Holding

Breath holding can be considered an extreme form of rebreathing in which there is no gas exchange between the outside atmosphere and the air within the lungs.

1. Click **Start,** wait a second or two, and then click **Breath Holding.**

2. Let the breath-holding activity continue for about 5 seconds, and then click **Normal Breathing.**

3. Click **Stop** when the tracing reaches the right edge of the oscilloscope.

What happened to the P_{CO_2} during breath holding?

_____

_____

What happened to the breathing pattern when normal respirations resume?

_____

_____

4. Click **Record Data.**

5. Click **Tools → Print Data** to print your data. ■

Histology Review Supplement

Turn to page 129 for a review of respiratory tissue.

Chemical and Physical Processes of Digestion

T he digestive system is a physiological marvel, composed of finely orchestrated chemical and physical activities. The food we ingest must be broken down to its molecular form for us to get the nutrients we need, and digestion involves a complex sequence of mechanical and chemical processes designed to achieve this goal as efficiently as possible. As food passes through the gastrointestinal tract, it is progressively broken down by the mechanical action of smooth muscle and the chemical action of enzymes until most nutrients have been extracted and absorbed into the blood.

Chemical Digestion of Foodstuffs: Enzymatic Action

Nutrients can only be absorbed when broken down into their monomer form, so food digestion is a prerequisite to food absorption.

   Enzymes are large protein molecules produced by body cells. They are biological **catalysts** that increase the rate of a chemical reaction without becoming part of the product. The digestive enzymes are hydrolytic enzymes, or **hydrolases,** which break down organic food molecules, or **substrates,** by adding water to the molecular bonds, thus cleaving the bonds between the subunits or monomers.

   A hydrolytic enzyme is highly specific in its action. Each enzyme hydrolyzes one or, at most, a small group of substrate molecules, and specific environmental conditions are necessary for an enzyme to function optimally. For example, temperature and pH have a large effect on the degree of enzymatic hydrolysis, and each enzyme has its preferred environment.

   Because digestive enzymes actually function outside the body cells in the digestive tract lumen, their hydrolytic activity can also be studied in a test tube. Such in vitro studies provide a convenient laboratory environment for investigating the effect of various factors on enzymatic activity.

Objectives

1. To list the digestive system enzymes involved in the digestion of proteins, fats, and carbohydrates; to state their site of origin; and to summarize the environmental conditions promoting their optimal functioning.

2. To recognize the variation between different types of enzyme assays.

3. To name the end products of digestion of proteins, fats, and carbohydrates.

4. To perform the appropriate chemical tests to determine if digestion of a particular food has occurred.

5. To cite the function(s) of bile in the digestive process.

6. To discuss the possible role of temperature and pH in the regulation of enzyme activity.

7. To define *enzyme, catalyst, control, substrate,* and *hydrolase.*

8. To explain why swallowing is both a voluntary and a reflex activity.

9. To discuss the role of the tongue, larynx, and gastroesophageal sphincter in swallowing.

10. To compare and contrast segmentation and peristalsis as mechanisms of propulsion.

Starch Digestion by Salivary Amylase

In this experiment you will investigate the hydrolysis of starch to maltose by salivary amylase, the enzyme produced by the salivary glands and secreted into the mouth. For you to be able to detect whether or not enzymatic action has occurred, you need to be able to identify the presence of these substances to determine to what extent hydrolysis has occurred. Thus, **controls** must be prepared to provide a known standard against which comparisons can be made. The controls will vary for each experiment and will be discussed in each enzyme section in this exercise.

Starch decreases and sugar increases as digestion proceeds according to the following equation:

$$\text{Starch} + \text{water} \xrightarrow{\text{amylase}} \text{X maltose}$$

Because the chemical changes that occur as starch is digested to maltose cannot be seen by the naked eye, you need to conduct an *enzyme assay,* the chemical method of detecting the presence of digested substances. You will perform two enzyme assays on each sample. The IKI assay detects the presence of starch and the Benedict's assay tests for the presence of reducing sugars, such as glucose or maltose, which are the digestion products of starch. Normally a caramel-colored solution, IKI turns blue-black in the presence of starch. Benedict's reagent is a bright blue solution that changes to green to orange to reddish-brown with increasing amounts of maltose. It is important to understand that enzyme assays only indicate the presence or absence of substances. It is up to you to analyze the results of the experiments to decide if enzymatic hydrolysis has occurred.

Choose **Chemical and Physical Processes of Digestion** from the main menu. The opening screen will appear in a few seconds (Figure 8.1). The *solutions shelf* in the upper right part of the screen contains the substances to be used in the experiment. The *incubation unit* beneath the solutions shelf contains a rack of test tube holders and the apparatus needed to run the experiments. Test tubes from the *test tube washer* on the left part of the screen are loaded into the rack in the incubation unit by clicking and holding the mouse button on the first tube, and then releasing (dragging-and-dropping) it into any position in the rack. The substances in the dropper bottles on the solutions shelf are dispensed by dragging-and-dropping the

Figure 8.1 Opening screen of the Amylase experiment.

dropper cap to a position over any test tube in the rack and then releasing it. During each dispensing event, five drops of solution drip into the test tube; then the dropper cap automatically returns to its position in the bottle.

Each test tube holder in the incubation unit not only supports but also allows you to boil the contents of a single test tube. Clicking the numbered button at the base of a test tube holder causes that single tube to descend into the incubation unit. To boil the contents of all tubes inside the incubation unit, click **Boil.** After they have been boiled, the tubes automatically rise. You can adjust the incubation temperature for the experiment by clicking the (**+**) or (**−**) buttons next to the Temperature window. Set the incubation time by clicking the (**+**) or (**−**) buttons next to the Timer window. Clicking the **Incubate** button starts the timer and causes the entire rack of tube holders to descend into the incubation unit where the tubes will be incubated at the temperature and the time indicated. While incubating, the tubes are automatically agitated to ensure that their contents are well mixed. During the experiment, elapsed time is displayed in the Elapsed Time window.

The cabinet doors in the *assay cabinet* above the test tube washer are closed at the beginning of the experiment, but they automatically open when the set time for incubation has elapsed. The assay cabinet contains the reagents and glassware needed to assay your experimental samples.

When you click the **Record Data** button in the *data control unit* at the bottom of the screen, your data is recorded in the computer's memory and displayed in the data grid at the bottom of the screen. Data displayed in the grid include the tube number, the three substances (additives) dispensed into each tube, whether or not a sample was boiled, the time and incubation temperature, and (**+**) or (**−**) marks indicating enzyme assay results. If you are not satisfied with a single run, you can click **Delete Run** to erase an experiment.

Once an experimental run is completed and you have recorded your data, discard the test tubes to prepare for a new run by dragging the used tubes to the large opening in the test tube washer. The test tubes will automatically be prepared for the next experiment.

Activity 1:
Assessing Starch Digestion by Salivary Amylase

Incubation

1.   Individually drag seven test tubes to the test tube holders in the incubation unit.

2.   Prepare tubes 1 through 7 with the substances indicated in Chart 1 below using the following approach.

•   Click and hold the mouse button on the dropper cap of the desired substance on the solutions shelf.

•   While still holding the mouse button down, drag the dropper cap to the top of the desired test tube.

•   Release the mouse button to dispense the substance. The dropper cap automatically returns to its bottle.

3.   When all tubes are prepared, click the number (**1**) under the first test tube. The tube will descend into the incubation unit. All other tubes should remain in the raised position.

4.   Click **Boil** to boil the number 1 tube. After boiling for a few moments, the tube will automatically rise.

5.   Now adjust the incubation temperature to 37°C and the timer to 60 min (compressed time) by clicking the (**+**) or (**−**) buttons.

6.   Click **Incubate** to start the run. The incubation unit will gently agitate the test tube rack, evenly mixing the contents of all test tubes throughout the incubation. Notice that the computer compresses the 60-minute time period into 60 seconds of real time, so what would be a 60-minute incubation in real life will take only 60 seconds in the simulation. When the incubation time elapses, the test tube rack will automatically rise, and the doors to the assay cabinet will open.

Chart 1	Salivary Amylase Digestion of Starch						
Tube no.	**1**	**2**	**3**	**4**	**5**	**6**	**7**
Additives	Amylase Starch pH 7.0 buffer	Amylase Starch pH 7.0 buffer	Amylase Deionized water pH 7.0 buffer	Deionized water Starch pH 7.0 buffer	Deionized water Maltose pH 7.0 buffer	Amylase Starch pH 2.0 buffer	Amylase Starch pH 9.0 buffer
Incubation condition	Boil first, then incubate at 37°C for 60 minutes	37°C	37°C	37°C	37°C	37°C	37°C
Benedict's test							
IKI test							

Assays

After the assay cabinet doors open, notice the two reagents in the assay cabinet. IKI tests for the presence of starch and Benedict's detects the presence of reducing sugars such as glucose or maltose, the digestion products of starch. Below the reagents are seven small assay tubes into which you will dispense a small amount of test solution from the incubated samples in the incubation unit, plus a drop of IKI.

1.   Click and hold the mouse on the first tube in the incubation unit. Notice that the mouse pointer is now a miniature test tube tilted to the left.

2.   While still holding the mouse button down, move the mouse pointer to the first small assay tube on the left side of the assay cabinet. Release the mouse button. Watch the first test tube automatically decant approximately half of its contents into the first assay tube on the left.

3.   Repeat steps 1 and 2 for the remaining tubes in the incubation unit, moving to a fresh assay tube each time.

4.   Next, click and hold the mouse on the IKI dropper cap and drag it to the first assay tube. Release the mouse button to dispense a drop of IKI into the first assay tube on the left. You will see IKI drip into the tube, which may cause a color change in the solution. A blue-black color indicates a **positive starch test.** If starch is not present, the mixture will look like diluted IKI, a **negative starch test.** Intermediate starch amounts result in a pale gray color.

5.   Now dispense IKI into the remaining assay tubes. Record your results (+ for positive, − for negative) in Chart 1.

6.   Dispense Benedict's reagent into the remaining mixture in each tube in the incubation unit by dragging-and-dropping the Benedict's dropper cap to the top of each test tube.

7.   After Benedict's reagent has been delivered to each tube in the incubation unit, click **Boil.** The entire tube rack will descend into the incubation unit and automatically boil the tube contents for a few moments.

8.   When the rack of tubes rises, inspect the tubes for color change. A green-to-reddish color indicates that a reducing sugar is present; this is a **positive sugar test.** An orange-colored sample contains more sugar than a green sample. A reddish-brown color indicates even more sugar. A negative sugar test is indicated by no color change from the original bright blue. Record your results in Chart 1.

9.   Click **Record Data** to display your results in the grid and retain your data in the computer's memory for later analysis. To repeat the experiment, drag all test tubes to the test tube washer and start again.

10.   Answer the following questions, referring to the chart (or the data grid in the simulation) as necessary. Hint: closely examine the IKI and Benedict's results for each tube.

What do tubes 2, 6, and 7 reveal about pH and amylase activity?

_____

_____

Which pH buffer allowed the highest amylase activity?

_____

Which tube indicates that the amylase did not contain maltose? _____

Which tubes indicate that the deionized water did not contain starch or maltose? _____

If we left out control tubes 3, 4, or 5, what objections could be raised to the statement: "Amylase digests starch to maltose"? (Hint: Think about the purity of the chemical solutions.)

_____

_____

_____

Would the amylase present in saliva be active in the stomach? Explain your answer.

_____

_____

What effect does boiling have on enzyme activity?

_____

_____

_____ ■

Activity 2:
Assessing Cellulose Digestion

If any test tubes are still in the incubator, click and drag them to the test tube washer before beginning this activity. In this activity, we will test to see whether amylase digests **cellulose.**

Incubation

1.   Individually drag seven test tubes to the test tube holders in the incubation unit.

2.   Prepare tubes 1 through 7 with the substances indicated in the chart on the next page using the following approach:

•   Click and hold the mouse button on the dropper cap of the desired substance on the solutions shelf.

•   While holding the mouse button down, drag the dropper cap to the top of the desired test tube.

•   Release the mouse button to dispense the substance. The dropper cap automatically returns to its bottle.

3.   When all tubes are prepared, click the number **(1)** under the first test tube. The tube will descend into the incubation unit.

4. Click **Freeze.** The tube's contents will be subjected to a temperature of −25°C. The tube will then automatically rise, with the contents of the tube frozen.

5. Adjust the incubation temperature to 37°C and the timer to 60 minutes by clicking the appropriate (+) or (−) buttons.

6. Click **Incubate** to start the run. The incubation unit will gently agitate the tubes as they incubate to thoroughly mix the tubes' contents. At the end of the incubation period, the tubes will ascend to their original positions on top of the incubator, and the doors to the assay cabinet will open.

Assays

When the assay cabinet opens, notice the two reagents in the cabinet. They are the same ones as in the previous activity: IKI will test for the presence of starch, while Benedict's solution will test for the presence of maltose. On the floor of the cabinet are seven small tubes that you will use to test the results of your experiment. The procedure will be identical to the one from the previous activity:

1. Click and hold the mouse on the first tube in the incubation unit. Notice that the mouse pointer is now a miniature test tube tilted to the left.

2. While still holding the mouse button down, move the mouse pointer to the first small assay tube on the left side of the assay cabinet. Release the mouse button.

3. Repeat steps 1 and 2 for the remaining tubes in the incubation unit, moving to a fresh assay tube each time.

4. Next, click and hold the mouse on the IKI dropper cap, and drag it to the first assay tube. Release the mouse button to dispense a drop of IKI into the first assay tube on the left. You will see IKI drip into the tube, which may cause a color change in the solution. A blue-black color indicates the presence of starch. If there is only a small amount of starch, you may see a pale gray color. If starch is not present, the mixture will look like diluted IKI.

5. Place IKI into the remaining assay tubes and note the color of each tube. Record your results in Chart 2.

6. Dispense Benedict's reagent into the remaining mixture in each tube in the incubation unit by dragging-and-dropping the Benedict's dropper cap to the top of each test tube.

7. After Benedict's reagent has been delivered to each tube in the incubation unit, click **Boil.** The entire tube rack will descend into the incubation unit and automatically boil the tube contents for a few moments.

8. When the rack of tubes rises, inspect the tubes for color change. A green to reddish color indicates that a reducing sugar is present for a positive sugar test. An orange sample indicates more sugar than the green color, while a reddish-brown indicates the highest amounts of sugar. If there has been no color change from the original blue, no sugar is present in the tube. Record your results in Chart 2.

9. Click **Record Data** to display your results in the grid and retain your data in the computer's memory for later analysis. To repeat the experiment, drag all test tubes to the test tube washer and start again.

10. Answer the following questions, referring to the chart.

Which tubes showed a positive test for the IKI reagent?

_____

Which tubes showed a positive test for the Benedict's

reagent? _____

What was the effect of freezing tube 1?

_____

How does the effect of freezing differ from the effect of boil-

ing? _____

_____

Chart 2	Enzyme Digestion of Starch and Cellulose						
Tube no.	**1**	**2**	**3**	**4**	**5**	**6**	**7**
Additives	Amylase Starch pH 7.0 buffer	Amylase Starch pH 7.0 buffer	Amylase Glucose pH 7.0 buffer	Amylase Cellulose pH 7.0 buffer	Amylase Cellulose Deionized water	Peptidase Starch pH 7.0 buffer	Bacteria Cellulose pH 7.0 buffer
Incubation condition	Freeze first, then incubate at 37°C for 60 minutes	37°C 60 min	37°C 60 min	37°C 60 min	37°C 60 min	37°C 60 min	37°C 60 min
Benedict's test							
IKI test							

What was the effect of amylase on glucose in tube 3? Can you offer an explanation for this effect? _____

_____

_____

What was the effect of amylase on cellulose in tube 4?

_____

_____

What can you conclude about the digestion of cellulose, judging from the results of test tubes 4, 5, and 7?

_____

_____

What was the effect of the different enzyme, peptidase, used in tube 6? Explain your answer, based on what you know about peptidase.

_____

_____

_____

11. Click **Tools → Print Data** to print your recorded data. ■

Protein Digestion by Pepsin

The chief cells of the stomach glands produce pepsin, a protein-digesting enzyme. Pepsin hydrolyzes proteins to small fragments (proteoses, peptones, and peptides). In this experiment, you will use BAPNA, a synthetic "protein" that is transparent and colorless when in solution. However, if an active, protein-digesting enzyme such as pepsin is present, the solution will become yellow. You can use this characteristic to detect pepsin activity: the solution turns yellow if the enzyme digests the BAPNA substrate; it remains colorless if pepsin is not active or not present. One advantage of using a synthetic substrate is that you do not need any additional indicator reagents to see enzyme activity.

Figure 8.2 Opening screen of the Pepsin experiment.

Choose **Pepsin** from the **Experiment** menu. The opening screen will appear in a few seconds (Figure 8.2). The solutions shelf, test tube washer, and incubation equipment are the same as in the amylase experiment; only the solutions have changed.

Data displayed in the grid include the tube number, the three substances dispensed into each tube, a (+) or (−) mark indicating whether or not a sample was boiled, the time and temperature of the incubation, and the optical density measurement indicating enzyme assay results.

Activity 3:
Assessing Protein Digestion by Pepsin

Pepsin Incubation

1. Individually drag six test tubes to the test tube holders in the incubation unit.

2. Prepare the tubes with the substances indicated in the chart below using the following method.

- Click and hold the mouse button on the dropper cap of the desired substance and drag the dropper cap to the top of the desired test tube.

- Release the mouse button to dispense the substance.

3. Once all tubes are prepared, click the number (**1**) under the first test tube. The tube will descend into the incubation unit. All other tubes should remain in the raised position.

4. Click **Boil** to boil tube 1. After boiling for a few moments, the tube will automatically rise.

5. Adjust the incubation temperature to 37°C and the timer to 60 minutes (compressed time) by clicking the (**+**) or (**−**) button.

6. Click **Incubate** to start the run. The incubation unit will gently agitate the test tube rack, evenly mixing the contents of all test tubes throughout the incubation. The computer is compressing the 60-minute time period into 60 seconds of real time. When the incubation time elapses, the test tube rack will automatically rise, and the doors to the assay cabinet will open.

Pepsin Assay

After the assay cabinet doors open, you will see an instrument called a spectrophotometer, which you will use to measure how much yellow dye was liberated by pepsin digestion of BAPNA. When a test tube is dragged to the holder in the spectrophotometer and the **Analyze** button is clicked, the instrument will shine a light through a specimen to measure the amount of light absorbed by the sample within the tube. The measure of the amount of light absorbed by the solution is known as its *optical density*. A colorless solution does not absorb light, whereas a colored solution has a relatively high light absorbance. For example, a colorless solution has an optical density of 0.0. A colored solution, however, absorbs some of the light emitted by the spectrophotometer, resulting in an optical density reading greater than zero.

In this experiment a yellow-colored solution is a direct indication of the amount of BAPNA digested by pepsin. Although you can visually estimate the yellow color produced by pepsin digestion of BAPNA, the spectrophotometer precisely measures how much BAPNA digestion occurred in the experiment.

1. Click and hold the mouse on the first tube in the incubation unit and drag it to the holder in the spectrophotometer.

2. Release the mouse button to drop the tube into the holder.

3. Click **Analyze.** You will see light shining through the solution in the test tube as the spectrophotometer measures its optical density. The optical density of the sample will be displayed in the optical density window below the Analyze button.

4. Record the optical density in Chart 3.

Chart 3	Pepsin Digestion of Protein					
Tube no.	**1**	**2**	**3**	**4**	**5**	**6**
Additives	Pepsin BAPNA pH 2.0 buffer	Pepsin BAPNA pH 2.0 buffer	Pepsin Deionized water pH 2.0 buffer	Deionized water BAPNA pH 2.0 buffer	Pepsin BAPNA pH 7.0 buffer	Pepsin BAPNA pH 9.0 buffer
Incubation condition	Boil first, then incubate at 37°C for 60 minutes	37°C 60 min	37°C 60 min	37°C 60 min	37°C 60 min	37°C 60 min
Optical density						

Chart 4	Pancreatic Lipase Digestion of Fats and the Action of Bile					
Tube no.	1	2	3	4	5	6
Additives	Lipase Vegetable oil Bile salts pH 7.0 buffer	Lipase Vegetable oil Deionized water pH 7.0 buffer	Lipase Deionized water Bile salts pH 9.0 buffer	Deionized water Vegetable oil Bile salts pH 7.0 buffer	Lipase Vegetable oil Bile salts pH 2.0 buffer	Lipase Vegetable oil Bile salts pH 9.0 buffer
Incubation condition	37°C 60 min	37°C 60 min	37°C 60 min	37°C 60 min	37°C 60 min	37°C 60 min
pH						

Can we determine if fat hydrolysis has occurred in tube 6?

_____ Explain your answer. _____

_____

Which pH resulted in maximum lipase activity? _____

Is this method of assay sufficient to determine if the optimum

activity of lipase is at pH 2.0? _____

In theory, would lipase be active in the mouth? _____

Would it be active in the stomach? _____

Explain your answers. _____

_____

Based on the enzyme pH optima you determined in Activities 1 through 4, where in the body would we expect to find the enzymes in these experiments?

Amylase _____

Pepsin _____

Lipase _____

8. Click **Tools** → **Print Data** to print your recorded data. ■

Physical Processes: Mechanisms of Food Propulsion and Mixing

Although enzyme activity is an essential part of the overall digestion process, food must also be processed physically by churning and chewing and moved by mechanical means along the tract if digestion and absorption are to be completed. Just about any time organs exhibit mobility, muscles are involved,

and movements of and in the gastrointestinal tract are no exception. Although we tend to think only of smooth muscles for visceral activities, both skeletal and smooth muscles are necessary in digestion. This fact is demonstrated by the simple trials in the next activity. Obtain the following materials:

- Water pitcher
- Paper cups
- Stethoscope
- Alcohol swabs
- Disposable autoclave bag

Activity 5:
Studying Mechanisms of Food Propulsion and Mixing
Deglutition (Swallowing)

Swallowing, or *deglutition,* which is largely the result of skeletal muscle activity, occurs in two phases: *buccal* (mouth) and *pharyngeal-esophageal.* The initial phase—the buccal—is voluntarily controlled and initiated by the tongue. Once begun, the process continues involuntarily in the pharynx and esophagus, through peristalsis, resulting in the delivery of the swallowed contents to the stomach.

1. While swallowing a mouthful of water from a paper cup, consciously note the movement of your tongue during the process. Record your observations.

_____

_____

_____

2. Repeat the swallowing process while your laboratory partner watches the externally visible movements of your larynx. This movement is more obvious in a male, who has a larger Adam's apple. Record your observations.

_____

_____

What do these movements accomplish? _____

_____

_____

3. Your lab partner should clean the ear pieces of a stethoscope with an alcohol swab and don the stethoscope. Then your lab partner should place the diaphragm of the stethoscope on your abdominal wall, approximately 1 inch below the xiphoid process and slightly to the left, to listen for sounds as you again take two or three swallows of water. There should be two audible sounds. The first sound occurs when the water splashes against the gastroesophageal sphincter. The second occurs when the peristaltic wave of the esophagus arrives at the sphincter and the sphincter opens, allowing water to gurgle into the stomach. Determine, as accurately as possible, the time interval between these two sounds and record it below.

Interval between arrival of water at the sphincter and the opening of the sphincter:

_____ sec.

This interval gives a fair indication of the time it takes for the peristaltic wave to travel down the 10-inch-long esophagus. Actually the time interval is slightly less than it seems because pressure causes the sphincter to relax before the peristaltic wave reaches it.

Dispose of the used paper cup in the autoclave bag. ▪

Segmentation and Peristalsis

Although several types of movement occur in the digestive tract organs, segmentation and peristalsis are most important as mixing and propulsive mechanisms.

Segmental movements are local constrictions of the organ wall that occur rhythmically. They serve mainly to mix the foodstuffs with digestive juices and to increase the rate of absorption by continually moving different portions of the chyme over adjacent regions of the intestinal wall. However, segmentation is an important means of food propulsion in the small intestine, and slow segmenting movements called haustral contractions are common in the large intestine.

Peristaltic movements are the major means of propelling food through most of the digestive viscera. Essentially they are waves of contraction followed by waves of relaxation that squeeze foodstuffs through the alimentary canal, and they are superimposed on segmental movements.

Histology Review Supplement

Turn to page 130 for a review of digestive tissue.

Renal System Physiology

Objectives

1. To define the following terms:

    glomerulus, glomerular capsule, renal corpuscle, renal tubule, nephron, proximal convoluted tubule, loop of Henle, and *distal convoluted tubule.*

2. To describe the blood supply to each nephron.

3. To identify the regions of the nephron involved in glomerular filtration and tubular reabsorption.

4. To study the factors affecting glomerular filtration.

5. To explore the concept of carrier transport maximum.

6. To understand how the hormones aldosterone and ADH affect the function of the kidney.

7. To describe how the kidneys can produce urine that is four times more concentrated than the blood.

Metabolism produces wastes that must be eliminated from the body. This excretory function is the job of the renal system, most importantly the paired kidneys. Each kidney consists of about one million nephrons that carry out two crucial services, blood filtration and fluid processing.

Microscopic Structure and Function of the Kidney

Each of the million or so **nephrons** in each kidney is a microscopic tubule consisting of two major parts: a glomerulus and a renal tubule. The **glomerulus** is a tangled capillary knot that filters fluid from the blood into the lumen of the renal tubule. The function of the **renal tubule** is to process that fluid, also called the **filtrate.** The beginning of the renal tubule is an enlarged end called the **glomerular capsule,** which surrounds the glomerulus and serves to funnel the filtrate into the rest of the renal tubule. Collectively, the glomerulus and the glomerular capsule are called the **renal corpuscle.**

As the rest of the renal tubule extends from the glomerular capsule, it becomes twisted and convoluted, then dips sharply down to form a hairpin loop, and then coils again before entering a collecting duct. Starting at the glomerular capsule, the anatomical parts of the renal tubule are as follows: the **proximal convoluted tubule,** the **loop of Henle** (nephron loop), and the **distal convoluted tubule.**

Two arterioles supply each glomerulus: an afferent arteriole feeds the glomerular capillary bed and an efferent arteriole drains it. These arterioles are responsible for blood flow through the glomerulus. Constricting the afferent arteriole lowers the downstream pressure in the glomerulus, whereas constricting the efferent arteriole will increase the pressure in the glomerulus. In addition, the diameter of the efferent arteriole is smaller than the diameter of the afferent arteriole, restricting blood flow out of the glomerulus. Consequently, the pressure in the glomerulus forces fluid through the endothelium of the glomerulus into the lumen of the surrounding glomerular capsule. In essence, everything in the blood except the cells and proteins are filtered through the glomerular wall. From the capsule, the filtrate moves into the rest of the renal tubule for processing. The job of the tubule is to reabsorb all the beneficial substances from its lumen while allowing the wastes to travel down the tubule for elimination from the body.

The nephron performs three important functions to process the filtrate into urine: glomerular filtration, tubular reabsorption, and tubular secretion. **Glomerular filtration** is a passive process in which fluid passes from the lumen of the glomerular capillary into the glomerular capsule of the renal tubule. **Tubular reabsorption** moves most of the filtrate back into the blood, leaving principally salt water plus the wastes in the lumen of the tubule. Some of the desirable or needed solutes are actively reabsorbed, and others move passively from the lumen of the tubule into the interstitial spaces. **Tubular secretion** is essentially the reverse of tubular reabsorption and is a process by which the kidneys can rid the blood of additional unwanted substances such as creatinine and ammonia.

The reabsorbed solutes and water that move into the interstitial space between the nephrons need to be returned to the blood, or the kidneys will rapidly swell like balloons. The peritubular capillaries surrounding the renal tubule reclaim the reabsorbed substances and return them to general circulation. Peritubular capillaries arise from the efferent arteriole exiting the glomerulus and empty into the veins leaving the kidney.

Simulating Glomerular Filtration

This computerized simulation allows you to explore one function of a single simulated nephron, glomerular filtration. The concepts you will learn by studying a single nephron can then be applied to understand the function of the kidney as a whole.

Choose **Renal System Physiology** from the main menu. The opening screen for the Simulating Glomerular Filtration experiment will appear in a few seconds (Figure 9.1). The main features on the screen when the program starts are a *simulated blood supply* at the left side of the screen, a *simulated nephron* within a supporting tank on the right side, and a *data control unit* at the bottom of the display.

Figure 9.1 Opening screen of the Simulating Glomerular Filtration experiment.

The left beaker is the "blood" source representing the general circulation supplying the nephron. The "blood pressure" in the beaker is adjustable by clicking the (+) and (−) buttons on top of the beaker. A tube with an adjustable radius called the *afferent flow* tube connects the left beaker to the simulated glomerulus. Another adjustable tube called the *efferent flow* tube drains the glomerulus. The afferent flow tube represents the afferent arteriole feeding the glomerulus of each nephron, and the efferent flow tube represents the efferent arteriole draining the glomerulus. The outflow of the nephron empties into a collecting duct, which in turn drains into another small beaker at the bottom right part of the screen. Clicking the valve at the end of the collecting duct (which currently reads **valve open**) stops the flow of fluid through the nephron and collecting duct.

The **Glomerular Pressure** window on top of the nephron tank displays the pressure within the glomerulus. The **Glomerular Filt. Rate** window indicates the flow rate of the fluid moving from the lumen of the glomerulus into the lumen of the renal tubule.

The concentration gradient bathing the nephron is fixed at 1200 milliosmoles (mosm). Clicking **Start** begins the experiment. Clicking **Refill** resets the equipment to begin another run.

The equipment in the lower part of the screen is called the *data control unit*. This equipment records and displays data you accumulate during the experiments. The data set for the first experiment (Afferent) is highlighted in the **Data Sets** window. You can add or delete a data set by clicking the appropriate button to the right of the Data Sets window. When you click **Record Data,** your data is recorded in the computer's memory and is displayed in the data grid. Data displayed in the data grid include the afferent radius, efferent radius, beaker pressure, glomerular pressure, glomerular filtration rate, and the urine volume. Clicking **Delete Line** allows you to discard data values for a single run, and clicking **Clear Data Set** erases the entire experiment to allow you to start over.

If you need help identifying any piece of equipment, choose **Balloons On** from the **Help** menu and move the mouse pointer onto any piece of equipment visible on the computer's screen. As the pointer touches the object, a pop-up window appears identifying the equipment. To close the pop-up window, move the mouse pointer away from the equipment. Choose **Balloons Off** to turn off this help feature.

Activity 1:
Investigating the Effect of Flow Tube Radius on Glomerular Filtration

Your first experiment will examine the effects of flow tube radii and pressures on the rate of glomerular filtration. Click **Start** to see the onscreen action. Continue when you understand how the simulation operates. Click **Refill** to reset the experiment.

1. The **Afferent** line in the **Data Sets** window of the data control unit should be highlighted in bright blue. If it is not, choose it by clicking the **Afferent** line. The data control unit will now record filtration rate variations due to changing afferent flow tube radius.

2. If the data grid is not empty, click **Clear Data Set** to discard all previous data.

3. Adjust the afferent radius to 0.35 mm, and the efferent radius to 0.40 mm by clicking the appropriate (+) or (−) buttons.

4. If the left beaker is not full, click **Refill.**

5. Keep the beaker pressure at 90 mm Hg during this part of the experiment.

6. Click **Start,** and watch the blood flow. Simultaneously, filtered fluid will be moving through the nephron and into the collecting duct. The Glomerular Filtration Rate window will display the fluid flow rate into the renal tubule when the left beaker has finished draining.

7. Now click **Record Data** to record the current experiment data in the data grid. Click **Refill** to replenish the left beaker and prepare the nephron for the next run.

8. Increase the afferent radius in 0.05-mm increments and repeat steps 6 through 8 until the maximum radius (0.60 mm) is achieved. Be sure to click **Record Data** after each trial. If you make an error and want to delete a single value, click the data line in the data grid and then click **Delete Line.**

What happens to the glomerular filtration rate as the afferent radius is increased?

_____

_____

Predict the effect of increasing or decreasing the efferent radius on glomerular filtration rate. Use the simulation to reach an answer if you are not sure.

_____

_____ ∎

Activity 2:
Studying the Effect of Pressure on Glomerular Filtration

Both the blood pressure supplying the glomerulus and the pressure in the renal tubule have a significant impact on the glomerular filtration rate. In this activity, the data control unit will record filtration rate variations due to changing pressure.

1. Click the **Pressure** line in the **Data Sets** window of the data control unit.

2. If the data grid is not empty, click **Clear Data Set** to discard all previous data.

3. If the left beaker is not full, click **Refill.**

4. Adjust the pressure in the left beaker to 70 mm Hg by clicking the appropriate (+) or (−) button.

5. During this part of the experiment, maintain the afferent flow tube radius at 0.55 mm and the efferent flow tube radius at 0.45 mm.

6. Click **Start,** and watch the blood flow. Filtrate will move through the nephron into the collecting duct. At the end of the run, the Glomerular Filtration Rate window will display the filtrate flow rate into the renal tubule.

7. Now click **Record Data** to record the current experiment data in the data grid. Click **Refill** to replenish the left beaker.

8. Increase the pressure in the upper beaker in increments of 10 mm Hg and repeat steps 6 through 8 until the maximum pressure (100 mm Hg) is achieved. Be sure to click **Record Data** after each trial. If you make an error and want to delete a single value, click the data line in the data grid and then click **Delete Line.**

What happened to the glomerular filtration rate as the beaker pressure was increased?

_____

_____

_____

Explain your answer.

_____

_____

_____

_____ ■

Activity 3:
Assessing Combined Effects on Glomerular Filtration

So far, you have examined the effects of flow tube radius and pressure on glomerular filtration rate. In this experiment you will be altering both variables to explore the combined effects on glomerular filtration rate and to see how one can compensate for the other to maintain an adequate glomerular filtration rate.

1. Click **Combined** in the **Data Sets** window of the data control unit.

2. If the data grid is not empty, click **Clear Data Set** to discard all previous data.

3. If the left beaker is not full, click **Refill.**

4. Set the starting conditions at

• 100 mm Hg beaker pressure

• 0.55 mm afferent radius

• 0.45 mm efferent radius

5. Click **Start.**

6. Now click **Record Data** to record the current baseline data in the data grid.

7. Click **Refill.**

You will use this baseline data to compare a run in which the valve at the end of the collecting duct is in the open position with a run in which the valve is in the closed position.

8. Use the simulation and your knowledge of basic renal anatomy to arrive at answers to the following questions. Be sure to click **Record Data** after each trial. If you make an error and want to delete a single value, click the data line in the data grid and then click **Delete Line.**

Click **valve open** on the end of the collecting duct. Note that it now reads **valve closed.** Click **Start,** and allow the run to complete.

How does this run compare to the runs in which the valve was open?

_____

Expanding on this concept, what might happen to total glomerular filtration and therefore urine production in a human kidney if all of its collecting ducts were totally blocked?

_____

_____

Would kidney function as a whole be affected if a single nephron was blocked? Explain.

_____

_____

Would the kidney be functioning if glomerular filtration was zero? Explain.

_____

_____

Explain how the body could increase glomerular filtration rate in a human kidney.

_____

_____

_____

_____

If you increased the pressure in the beaker, what other condition(s) could you adjust to keep the glomerular filtration rate constant?

_____

_____

9. Click **Tools** → **Print Data** to print your recorded data. ■

Simulating Urine Formation

This part of the computer simulation allows you to explore some aspects of urine formation by manipulating the interstitial solute concentration. Other activities include investigating the effects of aldosterone and ADH (antidiuretic hormone) and the role that glucose carrier proteins play in renal function.

Choose **Simulating Urine Formation** from the **Experiment** menu. The opening screen will appear in a few seconds (Figure 9.2). The basic features on the screen when the program starts are similar to the glomerular filtration screen. Most of the vascular controls have been moved off-screen to the left because they will not be needed in this set of experiments. Additional equipment includes *supply shelves* at the right side of the screen, a *glucose carrier control* located at the top of the nephron tank, and a *concentration probe* at the bottom left part of the screen.

The maximum concentration of the interstitial gradient to be dispensed into the tank surrounding the nephron is adjusted by clicking the (+) and (−) buttons next to the Conc. Grad. window. Click **Dispense** to fill the tank through the jets at the bottom of the tank with the chosen solute gradient. Click **Start** to begin a run. After a run completes, the concentration probe can be clicked and dragged over the nephron to display the solute concentration within.

Hormone is dispensed by dragging a hormone dropper cap to the gray cap button in the nephron tank at the top of the collecting duct and then letting go of the mouse button.

The (+) and (−) buttons in the glucose carrier control are used to adjust the number of glucose carriers that will be inserted into the simulated proximal convoluted tubule when the **Add Carriers** button is clicked.

Data displayed in the data grid will depend on which experiment is being conducted. Clicking **Delete Line** allows you to discard data values for a single run, and clicking **Clear Data Set** erases the entire experiment to allow you to start over.

Figure 9.2 Opening screen of the Simulating Urine Formation experiment.

Activity 4:
Exploring the Role of the Solute Gradient on Maximum Urine Concentration Achievable

In the process of urine formation, solutes and water move from the lumen of the nephron into the interstitial spaces. The passive movement of solutes and water from the lumen of the renal tubule into the interstitial spaces relies in part on the total solute gradient surrounding the nephron. When the nephron is permeable to solutes or water, an equilibrium will be reached between the interstitial fluid and the contents of the nephron. Antidiuretic hormone (ADH) increases the water permeability of the distal convoluted tubule and the collecting duct, allowing water to flow to areas of higher solute concentration, usually from the lumen of the nephron into the surrounding interstitial area. You will explore the process of passive reabsorption in this experiment. While doing this part of the simulation, assume that when ADH is present the conditions favor the formation of the most concentrated urine possible.

1. **Gradient** in the **Data Sets** window of the data control unit should be highlighted in bright blue. If it is not, then click **Gradient.**

2. If the data grid is not empty, click **Clear Data Set** to discard all previous data.

3. Click and hold the mouse button on the **ADH** bottle cap and drag it to the gray cap at the top right side of the nephron tank. Release the mouse button to dispense ADH onto the collecting duct.

4. Adjust the maximum total solute concentration of the gradient (**Conc. Grad.**) to 300 mosm by clicking the appropriate (+) or (−) button. Because the blood solute concentration is also 300 mosm, there is no osmotic difference between the lumen of the nephron and the surrounding interstitial fluid.

5. Click **Dispense.**

6. Click **Start** to begin the experiment. Filtrate will move through the nephron and then drain into the beaker below the collecting duct.

7. While the experiment is running, watch the **Probe.** When it turns red, click and hold the mouse on it, and drag it to the urine beaker. Observe the total solute concentration in the **Concentration** window.

8. Now click **Record Data** to record the current experiment data in the data grid.

9. Increase the maximum concentration of the gradient in 300-mosm increments, and repeat steps 3 through 8 until 1200 mosm is achieved. Be sure to click **Record Data** after each trial. If you make an error and want to delete a single value, click the data line in the data grid and then click **Delete Line.**

What happened to the urine concentration as the gradient concentration was increased?

_____

What factor limits the maximum possible urine concentration?

_____

_____

The solute concentration of the blood is about 300 mosm, and the highest interstitial solute concentration in a human kidney is about 1200 mosm. This means that the maximum urine solute concentration is about four times that of the blood. What would be the maximum possible urine concentration if the maximum interstitial solute concentration were 3000 mosm instead of 1200 mosm? Explain. (Use the simulation to arrive at an answer if you are not sure.)

_____

_____

_____

_____ ■

Activity 5:
Studying the Effect of Glucose Carrier Proteins on Glucose Reabsorption

Because carrier proteins are needed to move glucose from the lumen of the nephron into the interstitial spaces, there is a limit to the amount of glucose that can be reabsorbed. When all glucose carriers are bound with the glucose they are transporting, excess glucose is eliminated in urine. In this experiment, you will examine the effect of varying the number of glucose transport proteins in the proximal convoluted tubule.

1. Click **Glucose** in the **Data Sets** window of the data control unit.

2. If the data grid is not empty, click **Clear Data Set** to discard all previous data.

3. Set the concentration gradient (**Conc. Grad.**) to 1200 mosm.

4. Click **Dispense.**

5. Adjust the number of glucose carriers to 100 (an arbitrary figure) by clicking the appropriate (+) or (−) button.

6. Click **Add Carriers.** This action inserts the specified number of glucose carrier proteins per unit area into the membrane of the proximal convoluted tubule.

7. Click **Start** to begin the run after the carriers have been added.

8. Click **Record Data** to record the current experiment data in the data grid. Glucose presence in the urine will be displayed in the data grid.

9. Now increase the number of glucose carrier proteins in the proximal convoluted tubule in increments of 100 glucose carriers, and repeat steps 6 through 8 until the maximum

number of glucose carrier proteins (500) is achieved. Be sure to click **Record Data** after each trial. If you make an error and want to delete a single value, click the data line in the data grid and then click **Delete Line.**

What happened to the amount of glucose present in the urine as the number of glucose carriers was increased?

_____

_____

The amount of glucose present in normal urine is minimal because there are normally enough glucose carriers present to handle the "traffic." Predict the consequence in the urine if there was more glucose than could be transported by the available number of glucose carrier proteins.

_____

_____

Explain why we would expect to find glucose in the urine of a diabetic person.

_____

_____ ■

Activity 6:
Testing the Effect of Hormones on Urine Formation

The concentration of the urine excreted by our kidneys changes depending on our immediate needs. For example, if a person consumes a large quantity of water, the excess water will be eliminated, producing dilute urine. On the other hand, under conditions of dehydration, there is a clear benefit in being able to produce urine as concentrated as possible, thereby retaining precious water. Although the medullary gradient makes it possible to excrete concentrated urine, urine dilution or concentration is ultimately under hormonal control. In this experiment, you will investigate the effects of two different hormones on renal function, aldosterone produced by the adrenal gland and ADH manufactured by the hypothalamus and stored in the posterior pituitary gland. Aldosterone works to reabsorb sodium ions (and thereby water) at the expense of losing potassium ions; its site of action is the distal convoluted tubule. ADH makes the distal tubule and collecting duct more permeable to water, thereby allowing the body to reabsorb more water from the filtrate when it is present.

1. Click **Hormone** in the **Data Sets** window of the data control unit.

2. If the data grid is not empty, click **Clear Data Set** to discard all previous data.

3. During this part of the experiment, keep the concentration gradient at 1200 mosm.

4. Click **Dispense** to add the gradient, and then click **Start** to begin the experiment.

5. Now click **Record Data** to record the current experiment data in the data grid.

You will use this baseline data to compare with the conditions of the filtrate under the control of the two hormones.

6. Keeping all experiment conditions the same as before, do the following:

• Drag the **Aldosterone** dropper cap to the gray cap on the top right side of the nephron tank, and release the mouse to automatically dispense aldosterone into the tank surrounding the distal convoluted tubule and collecting duct.

• Click **Start,** and allow the run to complete.

• Click **Record Data.**

In this run, how does the volume of urine differ from the previously measured baseline volume?

_____

_____

Explain the difference in the total amount of potassium in the urine between this run and the baseline run.

_____

_____

7. Drag the **ADH** bottle cap to the gray cap on the top right side of the nephron tank, and release it to dispense ADH.

• Click **Start,** and allow the run to complete

• Click **Record Data.**

In this run, how does the volume of urine differ from the baseline measurement?

_____

_____

Is there a difference in the total amount of potassium in this run and the total amount of potassium in the baseline run? Explain your answer. (Hint: The urine volume with ADH present is about one-tenth the urine volume when it is not present.)

_____

_____

Are the effects of aldosterone and ADH similar or antag-

onistic? _____

Consider this situation: we want to reabsorb sodium ions but do not want to increase the volume of the blood by reabsorbing water from the filtrate. Assuming that aldosterone and ADH are both present, how would you adjust the hormones to accomplish the task?

_____

_____

_____

_____

If the interstitial gradient ranged from 300 mosm to 3000 mosm and ADH was not present, what would be the maximum possible urine concentration? _____

8. Click **Tools** → **Print Data** to print your recorded data. ▪

Histology Review Supplement

Turn to page 132 for a review of renal tissue.

Objectives

1. To define *pH*, and to identify the normal range of human blood pH levels.

2. To define *acid* and *base*, and to explain what characterizes each of the following: *strong acid, weak acid, strong base,* and *weak base*.

3. To explain how chemical and physiological buffering systems help regulate the body's pH levels.

4. To define the conditions of *acidosis* and *alkalosis*.

5. To explain the difference between *respiratory acidosis and alkalosis* and *metabolic acidosis and alkalosis*.

6. To understand the causes of respiratory acidosis and alkalosis.

7. To explain how the renal system compensates for respiratory acidosis and alkalosis.

8. To understand the causes of metabolic acidosis and alkalosis.

9. To explain how the respiratory system compensates for metabolic acidosis and alkalosis.

The term **pH** is used to denote the hydrogen ion concentration, $[H^+]$, in body fluids. The pH values are the reciprocal of $[H^+]$ and follow the formula

$$pH = \log(1/[H^+])$$

At a pH of 7.4, $[H^+]$ is about 40 nanomolars (n*M*) per liter. Because the relationship is reciprocal, $[H^+]$ is higher at *lower* pH values (indicating higher acid levels) and lower at *higher* pH values (indicating lower acid levels).

The pH of a body's fluids is also referred to as its **acid-base balance.** An **acid** is a substance that releases H^+ in solution (such as in body fluids). A **base,** often a hydroxyl ion (OH^-) or bicarbonate ion (HCO_3^-), is a substance that binds to H^+. A *strong acid* is one that completely dissociates in solution, releasing all of its hydrogen ions and thus lowering the solution's pH level. A *weak acid* dissociates incompletely and does not release all of its hydrogen ions in solution. A *strong base* has a strong tendency to bind to H^+, which has the effect of raising the pH value of the solution. A *weak base* binds less of the H^+, having a lesser effect on solution pH.

The body's pH levels are very tightly regulated. Blood and tissue fluids normally have pH values between 7.35 and 7.45. Under pathological conditions, blood pH values as low as 6.9 or as high as 7.8 have been recorded; however, values higher or lower than these cannot sustain human life. The narrow range of 7.35–7.45 is remarkable when one considers the vast number of biochemical reactions that take place in the body. The human body normally produces a large amount of H^+ as the result of metabolic processes, ingested acids, and the products of fat, sugar, and amino acid metabolism. The regulation of a relatively constant internal pH environment is one of the major physiological functions of the body's organ systems.

To maintain pH homeostasis, the body utilizes both *chemical* and *physiological* buffering sytems. Chemical buffers are composed of a mixture of weak acids and weak bases. They help regulate body pH levels by binding H^+ and removing it from solution as its concentration begins to rise or by releasing H^+ into solution as its concentration begins to fall. The body's three major chemical buffering systems are the *bicarbonate, phosphate,* and *protein buffer systems*. We will not focus on chemical buffering systems in this lab, but keep in mind that chemical buffers are the fastest form of compensation and can return pH to normal levels within a fraction of a second.

The body's two major physiological buffering systems are the renal and respiratory systems. The renal system is the slower of the two, taking hours to days to do its work. The respiratory system usually works within minutes but cannot handle the amount of pH change that the renal system can. These physiological buffer systems help regulate body pH by controlling the output of acids, bases, or CO_2 from the body. For example, if there is too much acid in the body, the renal system may respond by excreting more H^+ from the body in urine. Similarly, if there is too much carbon dioxide in the blood, the respiratory system may respond by breathing faster to expel the excess carbon dioxide. Carbon dioxide levels have a direct effect on pH levels because the addition of carbon dioxide to the blood results in the generation of more H^+. The following reaction shows what happens in the respiratory system when carbon dioxide combines with water in the blood:

$$H_2O + CO_2 \rightleftarrows \underset{\substack{\text{carbonic} \\ \text{acid}}}{H_2CO_3} \rightleftarrows H^+ + \underset{\substack{\text{bicarbonate} \\ \text{ion}}}{HCO_3^-}$$

This is a reversible reaction and is useful for remembering the relationships between CO_2 and H^+. Note that as more CO_2 accumulates in the blood (which frequently is caused by reduced gas exchange in the lungs), the reaction moves to the right and more H^+ is produced, lowering the pH:

$$H_2O + \mathbf{CO_2} \rightarrow \underset{\substack{\text{carbonic} \\ \text{acid}}}{H_2CO_3} \rightarrow \mathbf{H^+} + \underset{\substack{\text{bicarbonate} \\ \text{ion}}}{HCO_3^-}$$

Conversely, as $[H^+]$ increases, more carbon dioxide will be present in the blood:

$$H_2O + \mathbf{CO_2} \leftarrow \underset{\substack{\text{carbonic} \\ \text{acid}}}{H_2CO_3} \leftarrow \mathbf{H^+} + \underset{\substack{\text{bicarbonate} \\ \text{ion}}}{HCO_3^-}$$

Disruptions of acid-base balance occur when the body's pH levels fall below or above the normal pH range of 7.35–7.45. When pH levels fall below 7.35, the body is said to be in a state of **acidosis.** When pH levels rise above 7.45, the body is said to be in a state of **alkalosis. Respiratory acidosis** and **respiratory alkalosis** are the result of the respiratory system accumulating too much or too little carbon dioxide in the blood. **Metabolic acidosis** and **metabolic alkalosis** refer to all other conditions of acidosis and alkalosis (i.e., those not caused by the respiratory system). The experiments in this lab will focus on these disruptions of acid-base balance and on the physiological buffer systems (renal and respiratory) that compensate for such imbalances.

Respiratory Acidosis and Alkalosis

Respiratory acidosis is the result of impaired respiration, or *hypoventilation,* which leads to the accumulation of too much carbon dioxide in the blood. The causes of impaired respiration include airway obstruction, depression of the respiratory center in the brain stem, lung disease, and drug overdose. Recall that carbon dioxide acts as an acid by forming carbonic acid when it combines with water in the body's blood. The carbonic acid then forms hydrogen ions plus bicarbonate ions:

$$H_2O + \mathbf{CO_2} \rightarrow \underset{\substack{\text{carbonic} \\ \text{acid}}}{H_2CO_3} \rightarrow \mathbf{H^+} + \underset{\substack{\text{bicarbonate} \\ \text{ion}}}{HCO_3^-}$$

Because hypoventilation results in elevated carbon dioxide levels in the blood, the H^+ levels increase, and the pH value of the blood decreases.

Respiratory alkalosis is the condition of too little carbon dioxide in the blood. It is commonly the result of traveling to a high altitude (where the air contains less oxygen) or hyperventilation, which may be brought on by fever or anxiety. Hyperventilation removes more carbon dioxide from the blood, reducing the amount of H^+ in the blood and thus increasing the blood's pH level.

In this first set of activities, we focus on the causes of respiratory acidosis and alkalosis. From the main menu, select **Acid-Base Balance.** You will see the opening screen for the Respiratory Acidosis/Alkalosis experiment (Figure 10.1). If you have already completed Exercise 7 on respiratory system mechanics, this screen should look familiar. At the left is a pair of *simulated lungs,* which look like balloons, connected by a tube that looks like an upside-down Y. Air flows in and out of this tube, which simulates the trachea and other air passageways into the lungs. Beneath the "lungs" is a black platform simulating the diaphragm. The long, U-shaped tube containing red fluid represents blood flowing through the lungs. At the top left of the U-shaped tube is a pH meter that will measure the pH level of the blood once the experiment is begun. To the right is an *oscilloscope monitor,* which will graphically display respiratory volumes. Note that respiratory volumes are measured in liters (l) along the Y-axis, and time in seconds is measured along the X-axis. Below the monitor are three buttons: **Normal Breathing, Hyperventilation,** and **Rebreathing.** Clicking any one of these buttons will induce the given pattern of breathing. Next to these buttons are three data displays for P_{CO_2} (partial pressure of carbon dioxide in the blood)—these will give us the levels of carbon dioxide in the blood over the course of an experimental run. At the very bottom of the screen is the *data collection grid,* where you may record and view your data after each activity.

Activity 1: Normal Breathing

We will begin by observing what happens during normal breathing in order to establish baseline data.

1. Click **Start.** Notice that the **Normal Breathing** button dims, indicating that the simulated lungs are "breathing" normally. Also notice the reading in the pH meter at the top left, the readings in the P_{CO_2} displays, and the shape of the trace that starts running across the oscilloscope screen. As the trace runs, record the readings for pH at each of the following times:

At 20 seconds, pH = _____

At 40 seconds, pH = _____

At 60 seconds, pH = _____

2. Allow the trace to run all the way to the right side of the oscilloscope screen. At this point, the run will automatically end.

Figure 10.1 **Opening screen of the Respiratory Acidosis/Alkalosis experiment.**

3. Click **Record Data** at the bottom left to record your results.

4. Select **Print Graph** in the **Tools** menu.

5. Click **Clear Tracings** to clear the oscilloscope screen.

Did the pH level of the blood change at all during normal breathing? If so, how?

_____

Was the pH level always within the normal range for the human body?

_____

Did the P_{CO_2} level change during the course of normal breathing? If so, how?

_____ ∎

Activity 2a:
Hyperventilation—Run 1

Next, we will observe what happens to pH and carbon dioxide levels in the blood during hyperventilation.

1. Click **Start.** Allow the normal breathing trace to run for 10 seconds; then at the 10-second mark, click **Hyperventilation.** Watch the pH meter display, as well as the readings in the P_{CO_2} displays and the shape of the trace. As the trace runs, record the readings for pH at each of the following times:

At 20 seconds, pH = _____

At 40 seconds, pH = _____

At 60 seconds, pH = _____

2. Allow the trace to run all the way across the oscilloscope screen and end.

3. Click **Record Data.**

4. Select **Print Graph** from the **Tools** menu.

5. Click **Clear Tracings** to clear the oscilloscope screen.

Did the pH level of the blood change at all during this run? If so, how?

_____

_____

Was the pH level always within the normal range for the human body?

_____

_____

If not, when was the pH value outside of the normal range, and what acid-base imbalance did this pH value indicate?

_____

_____

Did the P_{CO_2} level change during the course of this run? If so, how?

_____

_____

If you observed an acid-base imbalance during this run, how would you expect the renal system to compensate for this condition?

_____

_____

How did the hyperventilation trace differ from the trace for normal breathing? Did the tidal volumes change?

_____

_____

What might cause a person to hyperventilate?

_____   ■

Activity 2b:
Hyperventilation—Run 2

This activity is a variation on Activity 2a.

1. Click **Start.** Allow the normal breathing trace to run for 10 seconds, then click **Hyperventilation** at the 10-second mark. Allow the hyperventilation trace to run for 10 seconds, then click **Normal Breathing** at the 20-second mark. Allow the trace to finish its run across the oscilloscope screen. Observe the changes in the pH meter and the P_{CO_2} displays.

2. Click **Record Data.**

3. Select **Print Graph** from the **Tools** menu.

4. Click **Clear Tracings** to clear the oscilloscope screen.

What happened to the trace after the 20-second mark when you stopped the hyperventilation? Did the breathing return to normal immediately? Explain your observation.

_____

_____

_____

_____   ■

Activity 3:
Rebreathing

Rebreathing is the action of breathing in air that was just expelled from the lungs. Breathing into a paper bag is an example of rebreathing. In this activity, we will observe what happens to pH and carbon dioxide levels in the blood during rebreathing.

1. Click **Start.** Allow the normal breathing trace to run for 10 seconds; then at the 10-second mark, click **Rebreathing.** Watch the pH meter display, as well as the readings in the P_{CO_2} displays and the shape of the trace. As the trace runs, record the readings for pH at each of the following times:

At 20 seconds, pH = _____

At 40 seconds, pH = _____

At 60 seconds, pH = _____

2. Allow the trace to run all the way across the oscilloscope screen and end.

3. Click **Record Data.**

4. Select **Print Graph** from the **Tools** menu.

5. Click **Clear Tracings** to clear the oscilloscope screen.

Did the pH level of the blood change at all during this run? If so, how?

_____

_____

Was the pH level always within the normal range for the human body?

_____

_____

If not, when was the pH value outside of the normal range, and what acid-base imbalance did this pH value indicate?

_____

_____

Did the P_{CO_2} level change during the course of this run? If so, how?

_____

If you observed an acid-base imbalance during this run, how would you expect the renal system to compensate for this condition?

_____

_____

How did the rebreathing trace differ from the trace for normal breathing? Did the tidal volumes change?

_____

_____

_____

Give examples of respiratory problems that would result in pH and P_{CO_2} patterns similar to what you observed during rebreathing.

_____

_____

_____

6. To print out all of the recorded data from this activity, click **Tools** and then **Print Data.** ■

In the next set of activities, we will focus on the body's primary mechanism of compensating for respiratory acidosis or alkalosis: renal compensation.

Renal System Compensation

The kidneys play a major role in maintaining fluid and electrolyte balance in the body's internal environment. By regulating the amount of water lost in the urine, the kidneys defend the body against excessive hydration or dehydration. By regulating the excretion of individual ions, the kidneys maintain normal electrolyte patterns of body fluids. By regulating the acidity of urine and the rate of electrolyte excretion, the kidneys maintain plasma pH levels within normal limits. Renal compensation is the body's primary method of compensating for conditions of respiratory acidosis or respiratory alkalosis. (Although the renal system also compensates for metabolic acidosis or metabolic alkalosis, a more immediate mechanism for compensating for metabolic acid-base imbalances is the respiratory system, as we will see in a later experiment.)

The activities in this section examine how the renal system compensates for respiratory acidosis or alkalosis. The primary variable we will be working with is P_{CO_2}. We will observe how increases and decreases in P_{CO_2} affect the levels of $[H^+]$ and $[HCO_3^-]$ that the kidneys excrete in urine.

Click on **Experiment** at the top of the screen, and select **Renal System Compensation.** You will see the screen shown in Figure 10.2. If you completed Exercise 9 on renal physiology, this screen should look familiar. There are two beakers on the left side of the screen, one of which is filled with blood, simulating the body's blood supply to the kidneys. Notice that the P_{CO_2} level is currently set to 40 and that the corresponding blood pH value is 7.4—both normal values. By clicking **Start,** you will initiate the process of delivering blood to the simulated nephron at the right side of the screen. As blood flows through the glomerulus of the

nephron, you will see the filtration from the plasma of everything except proteins and cells (note that the moving red dots in the animation do *not* include red blood cells). Blood will then drain from the glomerulus to the beaker at the right of the original beaker. At the end of the nephron tube, you will see the collection of urine in a small beaker. Keep in mind that although only one nephron is depicted here, there are actually over a million nephrons in each human kidney. Below the urine beaker are displays for H^+ and HCO_3^-, which will tell us the relative levels of these ions present in the urine.

Activity 4:
Renal Response to Normal Acid-Base Balance

1. Set the P_{CO_2} value to 40, if it is not already. (To increase or decrease P_{CO_2}, click the (**+**) or (**−**) buttons. Notice that as P_{CO_2} changes, so does the blood pH level.)

2. Click **Start,** and allow the run to finish.

3. At the end of the run, click **Record Data.**

At normal P_{CO_2} and pH levels, what level of H^+ was present

in the urine? _____

What level of $[HCO_3^-]$ was present in the urine? _____

Why does the blood pH value change as P_{CO_2} changes?

_____

_____

4. Click **Refill** to prepare for the next activity. ■

Activity 5:
Renal Response to Respiratory Alkalosis

In this activity, we will simulate respiratory alkalosis by setting the P_{CO_2} to values lower than normal (thus, blood pH will be *higher* than normal). We will then observe the renal system's response to these conditions.

1. Set P_{CO_2} to 35 by clicking the (**−**) button. Notice that the corresponding blood pH value is 7.5.

2. Click **Start.**

3. At the end of the run, click **Record Data.**

4. Click **Refill.**

5. Repeat steps 1 through 4, setting P_{CO_2} to increasingly lower values (i.e., set P_{CO_2} to 30 and then 20, the lowest value allowed).

What level of $[H^+]$ was present in the urine at each of these P_{CO_2}/pH levels?

_____

Figure 10.2 Opening screen of the Renal Compensation experiment.

What level of [HCO$_3^-$] was present in the urine at each of these P$_{CO_2}$/pH levels?

_____

_____

Recall that it may take hours or even days for the renal system to respond to disruptions in acid-base balance. Assuming that enough time has passed for the renal system to fully compensate for respiratory alkalosis, would you expect P$_{CO_2}$ levels to increase or decrease? Would you expect blood pH levels to increase or decrease?

_____

_____

Recall your activities in the first experiment on respiratory acidosis and alkalosis. Which type of breathing resulted in P$_{CO_2}$ levels closest to the ones we experimented with in this activity—normal breathing, hyperventilation, or rebreathing?

_____

Explain why this type of breathing resulted in alkalosis.

_____

_____

Activity 6:
Renal Response to Respiratory Acidosis

In this activity, we will simulate respiratory acidosis by setting the P_{CO_2} values higher than normal (thus, blood pH will be *lower* than normal). We will then observe the renal system's response to these conditions.

1. Make sure the left beaker is filled with blood. If not, click **Refill.**

2. Set P_{CO_2} to 60 by clicking the (+) button. Notice that the corresponding blood pH value is 7.3.

3. Click **Start.**

4. At the end of the run, click **Record Data.**

5. Click **Refill.**

6. Repeat steps 1 through 5, setting P_{CO_2} to increasingly higher values (i.e., set P_{CO_2} to 75 and then 90, the highest value allowed).

What level of $[H^+]$ was present in the urine at each of these P_{CO_2}/pH levels?

_____

_____

What level of $[HCO_3^-]$ was present in the urine at each of these P_{CO_2}/pH levels?

_____

_____

Recall that it may take hours or even days for the renal system to respond to disruptions in acid-base balance. Assuming that enough time has passed for the renal system to fully compensate for respiratory acidosis, would you expect P_{CO_2} levels to increase or decrease? Would you expect blood pH levels to increase or decrease?

_____

_____

Recall your activities in the first experiment on respiratory acidosis and alkalosis. Which type of breathing resulted in P_{CO_2} levels closest to the ones we experimented with in this activity—normal breathing, hyperventilation, or rebreathing?

_____

_____

Explain why this type of breathing resulted in acidosis.

_____

_____

7. Before going on to the next activity, select **Tools** and then **Print Data** in order to save a hard copy of your data results. ■

Metabolic Acidosis and Alkalosis

Conditions of acidosis or alkalosis that do not have respiratory causes are termed *metabolic acidosis* or *metabolic alkalosis*.

Metabolic acidosis is characterized by low plasma HCO_3^- and pH. The causes of metabolic acidosis include:

• *Ketoacidosis,* a buildup of keto acids that can result from diabetes mellitus

• *Salicylate poisoning,* a toxic condition resulting from ingestion of too much aspirin or oil of wintergreen (a substance often found in laboratories)

• The ingestion of too much alcohol, which metabolizes to acetic acid

• Diarrhea, which results in the loss of bicarbonate with the elimination of intestinal contents

• Strenuous exercise, which may cause a buildup of lactic acid from anaerobic muscle metabolism

Metabolic alkalosis is characterized by elevated plasma HCO_3^- and pH. The causes of metabolic alkalosis include:

• Alkali ingestion, such as antacids or bicarbonate

• Vomiting, which may result in the loss of too much H^+

• Constipation, which may result in reabsorption of elevated levels of HCO_3^-

Increases or decreases in the body's normal metabolic rate may also result in metabolic acidosis or alkalosis. Recall that carbon dioxide—a waste product of metabolism—mixes with water in plasma to form carbonic acid, which in turn forms H^+:

$$H_2O + \mathbf{CO_2} \rightarrow \underset{\substack{\text{carbonic} \\ \text{acid}}}{H_2CO_3} \rightarrow \mathbf{H^+} + \underset{\substack{\text{bicarbonate} \\ \text{ion}}}{HCO_3^-}$$

Therefore, an increase in the normal rate of metabolism would result in more carbon dioxide being formed as a metabolic waste product, resulting in the formation of more H^+—and thereby lowering plasma pH and potentially causing acidosis. Other acids that are also normal metabolic waste products, such as ketone bodies and phosphoric, uric, and lactic acids, would likewise accumulate with an increase in metabolic rate. Conversely, a decrease in the normal rate of metabolism would result in less carbon dioxide being formed as a metabolic waste product, resulting in the formation of less H^+—raising plasma pH and potentially causing alkalosis. Many factors can affect the rate of cell metabolism. For example, fever, stress, or the ingestion of food all cause the rate of cell metabolism to increase. Conversely, a fall in body temperature or a decrease in food intake causes the rate of cell metabolism to decrease.

The respiratory system compensates for metabolic acidosis or alkalosis by expelling or retaining carbon dioxide in the blood. During metabolic acidosis, respiration increases to expel carbon dioxide from the blood and decrease $[H^+]$ in order to raise the pH level. During metabolic alkalosis, respiration decreases to promote the accumulation of carbon dioxide in the blood, thus increasing $[H^+]$ and decreasing the pH level.

Figure 10.3 **Opening screen of the Metabolic Acidosis/Alkalosis experiment.**

The renal system also compensates for metabolic acidosis and alkalosis by conserving or excreting bicarbonate ions. However, in this set of activities we will focus on respiratory compensation of metabolic acidosis and alkalosis.

To begin, click **Experiment** at the top of the screen, and select **Metabolic Acidosis/Alkalosis.** The screen shown in Figure 10.3 will appear. This screen is similar to the screen from the first experiment; the main differences are the addition of a box representing the heart; tubes showing the double circulation of the heart; and a box representing the body's cells. The default "normal" metabolic rate has been set to 50 kcal/h—an arbitrary value, given that normal metabolic rates vary widely from individual to individual. The (+) and (−) buttons in the Body Cells box allow you to increase or decrease the body's metabolic rate. In the following activities, we will observe the respiratory response to acidosis or alkalosis brought on by increases or decreases in the body's metabolic rate.

Activity 7:
Respiratory Response to Normal Metabolism

We will begin by observing respiratory activity at normal metabolic conditions. This data will serve as a baseline against which we will compare our data in Activities 8 and 9.

1. Make sure the **Metabolic Rate** is set to 50, which for the purposes of this experiment we will consider the normal value.

2. Click **Start** to begin the experiment. Notice the arrows showing the direction of blood flow. A graph displaying respiratory activity will appear on the oscilloscope screen.

3.   After the graph has reached the end of the screen, the experiment will automatically stop. Note the data in the displays below the oscilloscope screen:

•   The **BPM** display gives you the *breaths per minute*—the rate at which respiration occurred.

•   **Blood pH** tells you the pH value of the blood.

•   **PCO₂** (shown as P_{CO_2} in the text) tells you the partial pressure of carbon dioxide in the blood.

•   **H⁺** and **HCO₃⁻** tell you the levels of each of these ions present.

4.   Click **Record Data**.

5.   Click **Tools** and then **Print Graph** in order to print your graph.

What is the respiratory rate? _____

Are the blood pH and P_{CO_2} values within normal ranges?

_____

6.   Click **Clear Tracings** before proceeding to the next activity. ■

Activity 8:
Respiratory Response to Increased Metabolism

1.   Increase the **Metabolic Rate** to 60 using the (**+**) button.

2.   Click **Start** to begin the experiment.

3.   Allow the graph to reach the end of the oscilloscope screen. Note the data in the displays below the oscilloscope screen.

4.   Click **Record Data**.

5.   Click **Tools** and then **Print Graph** in order to print your graph.

6.   Repeat steps 1 through 5 with the **Metabolic Rate** set at 70, and then 80.

As the body's metabolic rate increased:

How did respiration change?

_____

How did blood pH change?

_____

How did P_{CO_2} change?

_____

How did [H⁺] change?

_____

How did [HCO₃⁻] change?

_____

Explain why these changes took place as metabolic rate increased.

_____

_____

Which metabolic rates caused pH levels to decrease to a condition of metabolic acidosis?

_____

What were the pH values at each of these rates?

_____

By the time the respiratory system fully compensated for acidosis, how would you expect the pH values to change?

_____

7.   Click **Clear Tracings** before proceeding to the next activity. ■

Activity 9:
Respiratory Response to Decreased Metabolism

1.   Decrease the **Metabolic Rate** to 40.

2.   Click **Start** to begin the experiment.

3.   Allow the graph to reach the end of the oscilloscope screen. Note the data in the displays below the oscilloscope screen.

4.   Click **Record Data**.

5.   Click **Tools** and then **Print Graph** in order to print your graph.

6.   Repeat steps 1 through 5 with the **Metabolic Rate** set at 30, and then 20.

As the body's metabolic rate decreased:

How did respiration change?

_____

How did blood pH change?

_____

How did P$_{CO_2}$ change?

_____

How did [H$^+$] change?

_____

How did [HCO$_3^-$] change?

_____

Explain why these changes took place as the metabolic rate decreased.

_____

_____

_____

Which metabolic rates caused pH levels to increase to a condition of metabolic alkalosis?

_____

What were the pH values at each of these rates?

_____

By the time the respiratory system fully compensated for acidosis, how would you expect the pH values to change?

_____

7.   Click **Tools** → **Print Data** to print your recorded data. ■

Objectives

1. To become familiar with the "normal" values obtained with selected blood tests.

2. To understand how common laboratory procedures for examining blood can indicate pathology, or a state of disease.

3. To learn how the following blood tests are performed:

   hematocrit (packed cell volume) determination

   erythrocyte sedimentation rate

   hemoglobin determination

   blood typing

   total blood cholesterol determination

4. To understand what each of these procedures is measuring in a sample of blood.

5. To realize the importance of proper disposal of laboratory equipment that has come in contact with blood.

6. To understand the importance of matching blood types for blood transfusions.

B lood transports soluble substances to and from all cells of the body. Blood cells are also important in defense against pathogens. Laboratory analysis of the blood gives important information about how well these functions are being carried out.

This lab exercise consists of five common laboratory tests performed on blood: hematocrit determination; erythrocyte sedimentation rate; hemoglobin determination; blood typing; and total cholesterol determination.

Hematocrit Determination

Hematocrit refers to the percentage of red blood cells (RBCs) in a sample of whole blood. A hematocrit of 48 means that 48% of the volume of blood is red blood cells. Since the function of red blood cells is the transport of oxygen to the cells of the body, the higher the hematocrit, the more red blood cells are available to carry oxygen.

Hematocrit values are determined by spinning a microcapillary tube filled with a whole blood sample in a special microhematocrit centrifuge. This procedure separates the blood cells from the blood plasma and leaves a "buffy coat"

layer of white blood cells between the heavier red blood cell layer and the lighter plasma.

The hematocrit value can be determined after centrifuging by measuring the height of the layer of red cells in millimeters and dividing that number by the height of the initial column of blood to obtain the percentage of red blood cells.

The percentage of white blood cells can also be determined after centrifuging by comparing the height of the buffy coat to the initial height of the blood column.

The average hematocrit value for males is 47%, and the average for females is 42%. The normal upper limit is 55%. A lower-than-normal hematocrit indicates **anemia.** A higher-than-normal hematocrit indicates **polycythemia.**

Anemia is a condition in which insufficient oxygen is transported to the body's cells. There are many possible causes for anemia, including inadequate numbers of red blood cells, decreased amount of the oxygen-carrying pigment hemoglobin, abnormal hemoglobin, etc. The heme portion of hemoglobin molecules contains an atom of iron. If adequate iron is not available, the body cannot manufacture hemoglobin. This results in a condition called *iron deficiency anemia*. *Aplastic anemia* is the result of the failure of the bone marrow to produce adequate blood cells. *Pernicious anemia* is due to a lack of vitamin B_{12}, which is necessary for cell division. Intrinsic factor, produced by the stomach, allows absorption of vitamin B_{12}. Individuals who do not produce adequate intrinsic factor, or individuals who do not have adequate vitamin B_{12} in their diet, will suffer from pernicious anemia. *Sickle cell anemia* is an inherited condition in which the protein portion of hemoglobin molecules is folded incorrectly. As a result, oxygen molecules cannot fit with the misshapen hemoglobin, and anemia results.

Polycythemia refers to a significant increase in red blood cells. There are many possible causes of polycythemia, including living at high altitudes, strenuous athletic training, and tumors in the bone marrow.

In the following activity, we will simulate the blood test that is used to determine hematocrit. From the main menu, select **Blood Analysis.** You will see the opening screen for the Hematocrit Determination experiment (Figure 11.1).

To familiarize yourself with the equipment, select **Help** from the menu bar and then select **Balloons On.** This feature allows you to scroll around the screen and view equipment labels. You can turn the feature off by returning to **Help** and then selecting **Balloons Off.**

In the upper right portion of the screen is a dispenser containing six thin tubes, which are *heparinized capillary tubes*. Heparin is a substance that keeps blood from clotting. Below the capillary tubes are six test tubes containing samples of blood to be tested. When a capillary tube is dragged to a test tube of blood, it partially fills by fluid capillary action.

To the left of the samples of blood is a container of *capillary tube sealer* (a clay material, shown onscreen as an orange-yellow-colored substance.) The capillary tubes must

Figure 11.1   Opening screen of the Hematocrit Determination experiment.

be sealed on one end with this tube sealer so that the blood sample can be centrifuged without spraying out the blood.

When the tubes have been sealed, they are moved to slots in the *microhematocrit centrifuge*. When the **Start** button is clicked, the centrifuge will rotate at 14,500 revolutions per minute.

After the centrifuge stops and opens, the capillary tubes are moved, one at a time, next to the metric ruler on the upper left of the screen. When you click on the **Record Data** button next to the data table at the bottom of the screen, the following information about the sample will be recorded: the height of the column of blood in millimeters, the height of the red blood cell layer, the height of the buffy coat (white blood cells), the hematocrit (percent of red blood cells) and the percent of white blood cells.

In the lower left corner of the screen is a contaminated disposal container. Every piece of glassware that has come in contact with the blood must be disposed of by dragging it to this contaminated disposal container for proper disposal.

Activity 1:

Hematocrit Determination

The following individuals have contributed their blood for this test:

Sample 1: healthy male, living in Boston

Sample 2: healthy female, living in Boston

Sample 3: healthy male, living in Denver

Sample 4: healthy female, living in Denver

Sample 5: male with aplastic anemia

Sample 6: female with iron deficiency anemia

1.   Click and drag one heparinized capillary tube over to the test tube containing blood sample 1. Make sure the capillary tube is touching the blood. The capillary tube will fill itself by fluid capillary action.

2. Drag the capillary tube containing sample 1 to the container of capillary tube sealer to "seal" one end of the tube.

3. Drag the capillary tube to the microhematocrit centrifuge.

4. Repeat steps 1–3 for the remaining five samples of blood.

5. Set the timer for the centrifuge for 5 minutes by clicking the (+) button, and then click the **Start** button.

6. When the centrifuge stops and opens, click and drag capillary tube 1 to the metric ruler.

7. Click **Record Data** to record the information about sample 1.

8. Click and drag capillary tube 1 to the contaminated disposal container.

9. Repeat steps 6–8 for the remaining five capillary tubes in the centrifuge.

10. Click **Tools,** then **Print Data** to print the data from the table (or fill in Chart 1 at the bottom of the page):

If you wish to restart or repeat the lab, click the **Reset** button next to the data table.

What is the hematocrit value of a healthy male living at sea level in Boston?

_____

What is the hematocrit value of a healthy male living at one mile elevation in Denver?

_____

Is there as much oxygen in the air in Denver as there is in Boston?

_____

How do your kidneys respond to a decrease in blood oxygen? (Review this section in your textbook if necessary.)

_____

_____

If your bone marrow is producing an elevated number of red blood cells, what happens to your hematocrit?

_____

What is the hematocrit value of the male with aplastic anemia?

_____

Would the red blood cell count for an individual with aplastic anemia be higher, lower, or the same as the red blood cell count of a healthy individual?

_____

What is the hematocrit value of a healthy female living in Boston?

_____

Explain the difference in hematocrit values obtained from a healthy female living in Boston and a female with iron deficiency anemia.

_____

_____ ■

Erythrocyte Sedimentation Rate

The **erythrocyte sedimentation rate (ESR)** measures the settling of red blood cells in a vertical, stationary tube of blood during one hour.

In a healthy individual, red blood cells do not settle very much in an hour. In some disease conditions, increased production of fibrinogen and immunoglobulins cause the red blood cells to clump together, stack up, and form a column (called a *rouleaux formation*). Grouped like this, red blood cells are heavier and settle faster.

Chart 1					
Blood Sample	**Height of Column of Blood (mm)**	**Height of Red Blood Cell Layer (mm)**	**Height of Buffy Coat (White Blood Cells) (mm)**	**Hematocrit**	**% WBC**
1					
2					
3					
4					
5					
6					

Figure 11.2 **Opening screen of the Erythrocyte Sedimentation Rate experiment.**

This test is not a very specific or diagnostic test, but it can be used to follow the progression of certain disease conditions such as sickle cell anemia, certain cancers, and inflammatory diseases such as rheumatoid arthritis. When the disease worsens, the ESR increases; and when the disease improves, the ESR decreases. The ESR is elevated in iron deficiency anemia. Sometimes a menstruating female will develop anemia and show an increase in ESR.

The ESR can be used to evaluate a patient with chest pains: the ESR is elevated in established myocardial infarction (heart attack) but normal in angina pectoris. Similarly, it can be useful in screening a female patient with severe abdominal pains because the ESR is not elevated within the first 24 hours of acute appendicitis but is elevated in the early stage of acute pelvic inflammatory disease (PID) or ruptured ectopic pregnancy.

Click **Experiment** on the menu bar, then select **Erythrocyte Sedimentation Rate.** You will see the opening screen for the Erythrocyte Sedimentation Rate lab (Figure 11.2). Use the **Balloons On/Off** feature from the **Help** menu to familiarize yourself with the equipment on the screen.

In the upper left portion of the screen is a shelf with six samples of blood that have been treated with the anticoagulant heparin. Also on the shelf is a dropper bottle of sodium citrate. The sodium citrate is used to dilute the blood samples so they can easily be poured into the narrow sedimentation rate tubes (used later in the lab).

Below the shelf is a test tube dispenser and a test tube rack. To the right of the test tube rack is a cabinet that contains six sedimentation tubes. This cabinet will open when all six blood samples have been added to the test tubes and diluted with sodium citrate. Below this cabinet is a timer, a window showing elapsed time, and a **Start** button to start the timer.

In the upper right portion of the screen is a magnifying chamber that will help you read the millimeter markings on the sedimentation tubes.

In the lower right portion of the screen is a contaminated disposal container. All glassware that has come in contact with the blood must be placed in this container for proper disposal.

When you click on the **Record Data** button next to the data table at the bottom of the screen, the following information about the sample will be recorded: distance RBCs have settled, time elapsed, and sedimentation rate.

Activity 2:
Erythrocyte Sedimentation Rate

The following individuals have contributed their blood for this test:

Sample 1: healthy individual

Sample 2: menstruating female

Sample 3: person with sickle cell anemia

Sample 4: person with iron deficiency anemia

Sample 5: person suffering a myocardial infarction

Sample 6: person suffering angina pectoris

1.   Individually click and drag six test tubes from the dispenser to the test tube rack.

2.   Click on the dropper for blood sample 1, and drag it to the first test tube. One milliliter of blood will be dispensed into the tube.

3.   Repeat step 2 for the remaining five samples of blood, using a different test tube for each sample.

4.   Click on the dropper for the **3.8% sodium citrate,** and drag it over the test tube containing blood sample 1; 0.5 milliliter of sodium citrate will be dispensed into the tube.

5.   Repeat step 4 for the other five samples of blood (that is, add sodium citrate to tubes 2–6).

6.   Click on the **Mix** button. The samples will automatically mix for a few seconds.

7.   After the samples have been mixed, the cabinet with six sedimentation tubes will open.

8.   Click on the tube containing blood sample 1. Notice that the pointer is now a small test tube pointed to the left.

9.   While still holding the mouse button down, move the mouse pointer to the first sedimentation tube in the cabinet. The contents of the small test tube will pour into the sedimentation tube.

10.   Click and drag the now empty test tube to the contaminated disposal container.

11.   Repeat steps 8–10 with the other five samples of blood.

12.   When the six sedimentation tubes are filled, set the timer for 60 minutes by clicking the (**+**) button, and then click the **Start** button.

13.   After 60 minutes have elapsed, drag sedimentation tube 1 to the magnifying chamber at the top right of the screen. Examine the tube. The tube is marked in millimeters, and the distance between two marks is 5 mm. How many millimeters has the blood settled?

_____

What is in the beige colored portion of the tube? _____

14.   Click the **Record Data** button next to the data table. The distance in millimeters that the red blood cells have settled, the elapsed time, and the sedimentation rate will be entered in the table.

15.   Drag the sedimentation tube to the contaminated disposal container.

16.   Repeat steps 13–15 with the other five sedimentation tubes.

17.   Click **Tools,** then **Print Data** to print the data from the table, or fill in Chart 2 at the bottom of this page:

Did the person with sickle cell anemia show an elevated ESR?

_____

How did the ESR for a person with iron deficiency anemia compare to the ESR for a healthy individual?

_____

Explain the ESR for sample 2, the menstruating female.

_____

Explain the ESRs for samples 5 and 6 (the patients suffering from myocardial infarction and angina pectoris, respectively.)

_____

_____ ∎

Chart 2			
Blood Sample	**Distance RBCs Have Settled (mm)**	**Elapsed Time**	**Sedimentation Rate**
1			
2			
3			
4			
5			
6			

Figure 11.3 **Opening screen of the Hemoglobin Determination experiment.**

Hemoglobin

Hemoglobin (Hb), a protein found in red blood cells, is necessary for the transport of oxygen from the lungs to the body's cells. Anemia results when insufficient oxygen is carried in the blood.

Hemoglobin molecules consist of four polypeptide chains of amino acids, the "globin" part of the molecule. Each polypeptide chain has a heme unit—a group of atoms, which includes an atom of iron. When the polypeptide chain folds up correctly, it has an appropriate shape to bind with a molecule of oxygen. So, each hemoglobin molecule can carry four molecules of oxygen. Oxygen combined with hemoglobin forms oxyhemoglobin, which has a bright red color.

A quantitative hemoglobin determination is useful for determining the classification and possible causes of anemia and gives useful information on some other disease conditions. For example, a person can have anemia with a normal red blood cell count, if there is inadequate hemoglobin in the red blood cells.

Normal blood contains 12 to 18 grams of hemoglobin per 100 milliliters of blood. A healthy male has 13.5 to 18 g/100 ml;

a healthy female has 12 to 16 g/100 ml. Hemoglobin values increase in patients with polycythemia, congestive heart failure, and chronic obstructive pulmonary disease (COPD). They also increase at high altitudes. Hemoglobin values decrease in patients with anemia, hyperthyroidism, cirrhosis of the liver, renal disease, systemic lupus erythematosus, and severe hemorrhage.

The hemoglobin content of a sample of blood can be determined by stirring the blood with a wooden stick to rupture, or lyse, the cells. The intensity of the color of the lysed blood is a result of the amount of hemoglobin present. A *hemoglobinometer* compares the color of the sample to standard values to determine the hemoglobin content of the sample. The hemoglobinometer transmits green light through the hemolyzed blood sample. The amount of light that passes through the sample is compared to standard color intensities. Green light is used because the human eye is able to easily detect subtle differences in green colors.

From the **Experiment** menu, select **Hemoglobin Determination.** You will see the opening screen for the Hemoglobin Determination lab (Figure 11.3). Use the **Balloons On/Off** feature from the **Help** menu to familiarize yourself with the equipment on the screen.

In the upper right portion of the screen is a shelf with five samples of blood.

In the middle of the screen is a lab table and a container of hemolysis sticks. The hemolysis sticks will be used to stir the blood samples to lyse the red blood cells, thereby releasing their hemoglobin.

In the bottom left of the screen is a blood chamber dispenser that provides a slide with a depression to receive the blood sample.

Above the blood chamber dispenser is a hemoglobinometer. The hemoglobinometer has a black rectangular slot to receive the blood chamber and an **Eject** button to remove the blood chamber. When the loaded blood chamber is inserted into the slot, the hemoglobinometer view will change to show a split screen that compares the color of the hemolyzed blood sample to a standard color for which given levels of hemoglobin are already known. A window on the hemoglobinometer displays the grams of hemoglobin per 100 milliliters of blood. A small handle on the top right of the hemoglobinometer can be slid down until the colors shown on the device match the colors of the sample of blood to be tested.

When you click on the **Record Data** button next to the data table at the bottom of the screen, the grams of hemoglobin per 100 milliliters of blood will be recorded.

In the lower right portion of the screen is a contaminated disposal container. All glassware and hemolysis sticks that have come in contact with the blood must be placed in this container for proper disposal.

Activity 3:
Hemoglobin(Hb) Determination

The following individuals have contributed their blood for this test:

Sample 1: healthy male

Sample 2: healthy female

Sample 3: female with iron deficiency anemia

Sample 4: male with polycythemia

Sample 5: female Olympic athlete

1. Click and drag a clean blood chamber slide from the blood chamber dispenser to the lab table.

2. Click on the dropper for blood sample 1, and drag it over to the depression on the blood chamber slide. A drop of blood will be dispensed into the depression.

3. Click a hemolysis stick, and drag it to the drop of blood. The stick will stir the blood sample for 45 seconds, lysing the red blood cells and releasing their hemoglobin.

4. Drag the hemolysis stick to the contaminated disposal container.

5. Drag the blood chamber slide to the dark rectangular slot on the hemoglobinometer.

6. You will see a pop-up window appear, displaying the view inside the hemoglobinometer. The left half of the circular field shows the intensity of green light transmitted by blood sample 1. The right half of the circular field shows the intensity of green light for known levels of hemoglobin present in blood.

7. Click the lever on the top right of the hemoglobinometer, and slowly drag it downward until the right half of the field matches the shade of green on the left side of the field.

8. Click the **Record Data** button next to the data table to record the grams of hemoglobin per 100 milliliters of blood for blood sample 1. Click "X" to close the pop-up window.

9. Click the **Eject** button to remove the blood chamber with blood sample 1 from the hemoglobinometer.

10. Drag the blood sample 1 chamber to the contaminated disposal container.

11. Repeat steps 1–10 for the remaining samples of blood.

Fill in Chart 3 (below), using the grams of hemoglobin per 100 milliliters of blood that you obtained in this exercise. Use the packed cell volume (PCV) data provided below to calculate the ratio of PCV to Hb. (A calculator is available by clicking on the **Tools** menu.)

An individual might have a normal or near normal hematocrit value (packed cell volume) and still suffer from anemia if the red blood cells do not contain adequate hemoglobin. A normal ratio of packed cell volume to grams of hemoglobin is approximately 3:1.

Chart 3

Blood Sample	gm Hb/100 ml blood	Hematocrit (PCV)	Ratio of PCV to Hb
Healthy male		48	
Healthy female		44	
Female with iron deficiency anemia		40	
Male with polycythemia		60	
Female Olympic athlete		60	

What is the normal hematocrit value for a healthy male?

_____

What is the normal hematocrit value for a healthy female?

_____

What does the ratio of PCV to Hb tell you about the red blood cells of the female with iron deficiency anemia?

_____

Does the male with polycythemia have a normal ratio of PCV

to Hb? _____

Based on these results, do you think his red blood cells contain adequate quantities of hemoglobin molecules? Why?

_____

_____

Does the female Olympic athlete have a normal ratio of PCV

to Hb? _____

Based on these results, do you think her red blood cells contain adequate quantities of hemoglobin molecules? Why?

_____

_____

Blood Typing

All of the cells in the human body, including the red blood cells, are surrounded by a *plasma (cell) membrane*. The plasma membrane contains genetically determined glycoproteins, called antigens, that identify the cells. On red blood cell membranes, these antigens are called *agglutinogens*.

It is important to determine blood types before performing blood transfusions in order to avoid mixing incompatible blood. Although many different antigens are present on red blood cell membranes, the ABO and Rh antigens cause the most vigorous and potentially fatal transfusion reactions. If a blood transfusion recipient has antibodies (called *agglutinins*) to the antigens present on the transfused cells, the red blood cells will be clumped together, or *agglutinated,* and then lysed. This results in a potentially life-threatening blood transfusion reaction.

The ABO blood groups are determined by the presence or absence of two antigens: type A and type B. These antigens are genetically determined so a person has two copies (alleles) of the gene for these proteins, one copy from each parent. The presence of these antigens is due to a dominant gene, and their absence is due to a recessive gene.

- A person with type A blood can have two gene alleles for the A antigen, or that person could have one gene allele for type A antigen and the other allele for the absence of either A or B antigen.

- A person with type B blood can have two gene alleles for the B antigen, or that person could have one gene allele for type B antigen and the other allele for the absence of either A or B antigen.

- A person with type AB blood has one gene allele for the A antigen and the other allele for the B antigen.

- A person with type O blood will have inherited two recessive gene alleles and has neither type A nor type B antigen.

Antibodies to the A and B antigens are found pre-formed in the blood plasma. These antibodies will interact with the antigens that are not present, so a person with type A blood will have anti-B antibodies. This is summarized in the following chart:

Chart 4		
Antigens on Blood Type	**Antibodies in RBCs**	**Plasma**
A	A	anti-B
B	B	anti-A
AB	A and B	none
O	none	anti-A and anti-B

The Rh factor is another genetically determined protein that may be present on red blood cell membranes. Approximately 85% of the population is Rh positive and has this protein. Antibodies to the Rh factor are not found pre-formed in the plasma. These antibodies are produced only after exposure to the Rh factor by persons who are Rh negative.

Separate drops of a blood sample are mixed with antisera containing antibodies to the types A and B antigens and antibodies to the Rh factor. An agglutination reaction (showing clumping) indicates the presence of the proteins.

In this experiment, we will be conducting blood typing tests on six blood samples. From the **Experiment** menu, select **Blood Typing.** You will see the opening screen for the Blood Typing lab (Figure 11.4). Use the **Balloons On/Off** feature from the **Help** menu to familiarize yourself with the equipment on the screen.

In the upper right portion of the screen is a shelf with six samples of blood.

In the upper left portion of the screen is a shelf containing bottles of anti-A serum (blue color), anti-B serum (yellow color), and anti-Rh serum (white color). These bottles contain antibodies to the A antigen, B antigen, and Rh antigen, respectively.

Figure 11.4 Opening screen of the Blood Typing experiment.

In the center of the screen is a lab table for performing the blood typing. To the left of the lab table is a blood typing slide dispenser.

Above the blood typing slide dispenser is a container of stirring sticks. These sticks are color coded: the blue stick is to be used with the anti-A serum, the yellow stick is to be used with the anti-B serum, and the white stick is to be used with the anti-Rh serum.

To the right of the lab table is a *light box* for viewing the blood type samples. When you click on the **Light** button, the screen above unrolls to display the blood types.

To the left of the light box is a data table to record your results.

In the bottom right portion of the screen is a contaminated disposal container. All glassware and sticks that have come in contact with blood must be placed in this container for proper disposal.

Activity 4:
Blood Typing

Six individuals with different blood types have donated their blood for this exercise.

1. Click and drag a blood typing slide from the blood typing slide dispenser to the lab table. Note that the three wells on the slide are labeled "A," "B," and "Rh."

2. Click on the dropper for blood sample 1, and drag it over the well labeled A on the blood typing slide. A drop of blood will be dispensed into the well.

3. Repeat step 2 to deposit drops of blood from sample 1 in the two remaining wells on the blood typing slide.

4. Click on the dropper for anti-A serum, and drag it over the well labeled A on the blood typing slide. A drop of anti-A serum will be dispensed into the well.

5. Repeat step 4 with the anti-B serum. Be sure to dispense it into the well labeled B.

6. Repeat step 4 with the anti-Rh serum. Be sure to dispense it into the well labeled Rh.

7. Obtain a blue-tipped stirring stick, and drag it to well A. It will mix the blood and anti-A serum.

8. Dispose of the stirring stick into the contaminated disposal container.

9. Select a yellow-tipped stirring stick, and drag it to well B.

10. Dispose of the stirring stick into the contaminated disposal container.

11. Select a white-tipped stirring stick, and drag it to well Rh.

12. Dispose of the stirring stick properly into the contaminated disposal container.

13. Drag the blood typing slide to the light box, and click the **Light** button. The screen will unroll, displaying the results of the blood typing.

14. Examine the results labeled A on the screen. If coagulation (agglutination, or "clumpiness") is present, click on **Positive.** If no coagulation is present (the sample will look smooth), click on **Negative.**

15. Repeat step 14 for the results labeled B and Rh. In each case, choose **Positive** if the sample is coagulated and **Negative** if the sample is not coagulated.

16. Click the **Record Data** button on the data table to record the results of blood sample one.

17. Click and drag the blood typing slide to the contaminated disposal container.

18. Click the **X** at the top right of the scroll to close the scroll.

19. Repeat steps 1–18 for the remaining samples of blood.

Using the data you have collected in this activity, determine the blood type of each sample and fill in Chart 5 at the bottom of the page: (Indicate coagulation as either "positive" or "negative.")

If the anti-A antibody causes the blood to coagulate, which antigen would be present on the blood cells?

_____

If a person has type AB blood, which antigens are present on the red blood cells?

_____

Which antibodies are present in the plasma of a person with type AB blood?

_____

Does a person with type O blood have A or B antigens on the red blood cells?

_____ ■

Blood Cholesterol

Cholesterol is a lipid substance that is essential for life. It is an important component of all cell membranes and is the basis for making steroid hormones, vitamin D, and bile salts.

Cholesterol is produced in the human liver and is present in some foods of animal origin, such as milk, meat, and eggs. Since cholesterol is a water-insoluble lipid, it needs to be wrapped in protein packages, called lipoproteins, to travel in the watery blood from the liver and digestive organs to the cells of the body.

One type of lipoprotein package, called LDL (low density liproprotein), has been identified as a potential source of damage to the interior of arteries, resulting in the build-up of plaque, or atherosclerosis, in these blood vessels. A total blood cholesterol determination does not measure the level of LDLs, but it does provide valuable information about the total amount of cholesterol in the blood.

Less than 200 milligrams of total cholesterol per deciliter of blood is considered desirable. Between 200 to 239 mg/dL is considered borderline high cholesterol. Over 240 mg/dL is considered high blood cholesterol and is associated with increased risk of cardiovascular disease. Abnormally low blood levels of cholesterol (total cholesterol lower than 100 mg/dL) can also be a problem. Low levels may indicate hyperthyroidism (overactive thyroid gland), liver disease, inadequate absorption of nutrients from the intestine, or

Chart 5				
Blood Sample	**Coagulation with Anti-A Serum**	**Coagulation with Anti-B Serum**	**Coagulation with Anti-Rh Serum**	**Blood Type**
1				
2				
3				
4				
5				
6				

Figure 11.5 Opening screen of the Total Cholesterol Determination experiment.

malnutrition. Other reports link hypocholesterolemia (low blood cholesterol) to depression, anxiety, and mood disturbances, which are thought to be controlled by the level of available serotonin, a neurotransmitter. There is evidence of a relationship between low levels of blood cholesterol and low levels of serotonin in the brain.

In this test for total blood cholesterol, a sample of blood is mixed with enzymes that produce a colored reaction with cholesterol. The intensity of the color indicates the amount of cholesterol present. The cholesterol tester compares the color of the sample to the colors of known levels of cholesterol (standard values).

From the **Experiment** menu, select **Total Cholesterol Determination.** You will see the opening screen for the Total Cholesterol Determination lab (Figure 11.5). Use the **Balloons On/Off** feature from the **Help** menu to familiarize yourself with the equipment on the screen.

In the upper right portion of the screen is a dispenser of *lancets,* sharp needlelike instruments that are used to prick the finger to obtain a drop of blood.

Beneath the lancet dispenser is a patient's finger. The patient can be changed by clicking the **Next Patient** button beneath the finger.

On top of the data table is a container of alcohol wipes for cleansing the finger tip before it is punctured with the lancet.

The left portion of the screen shows a cabinet containing a *color wheel* that is divided into sections showing different intensities of green. Each shade of green corresponds to a range of total cholesterol levels. Below the cabinet is a timer that can be set for 1 to 3 minutes.

In the upper left portion of the screen is a cholesterol strip dispenser. These cholesterol strips contain chemicals that convert, by a series of reactions, the cholesterol in the blood sample into a green-colored solution. These reactions take 3 minutes. By matching the color of the cholesterol strip to a color on the color wheel, we can determine the cholesterol level of a given blood sample. Higher levels of cholesterol will result in a deeper green color.

The bottom of the screen has a data table for recording the total cholesterol level of the blood samples.

In the lower right portion of the screen is a contaminated disposal container. Any piece of equipment that has come into contact with the blood must be disposed of properly by dragging it to this contaminated disposal container.

Activity 5:
Total Cholesterol Determination

1. Click and drag an alcohol wipe over the end of patient 1's finger.

2. Click and drag a lancet to the tip of the finger. The lancet will prick the finger to obtain a drop of blood.

3. Drag the lancet to the contaminated disposal container.

4. Drag a cholesterol strip to the finger. The blood should transfer to the strip.

5. Drag the cholesterol strip to the rectangular area to the right of the color wheel.

6. Set the timer for 3 minutes, and click **Start.** Notice that the strip begins to change color.

7. After 3 minutes, decide which color on the color wheel most closely matches the color on the cholesterol test strip. Click on that color. It is sometimes difficult to match the color on the cholesterol strip with the appropriate color on the color wheel. If the color you have chosen is not the exact match, you will see a pop-up window asking you to try again.

8. Click on **Record Data** to record this information in the data table.

9. Drag the cholesterol test strip from patient 1 to the contaminated disposal container.

10. Click **Next Patient** to expose the finger of patient 2.

11. Repeat steps 1–10 for the next patient.

12. There are a total of four patients. Repeat steps 1–10 until you have collected data for all four patients.

What health problems might be in store for patient 2, based on these results?

_____

What advice about diet and exercise would you give patient 4?

_____ ■

Serological Testing

Objectives

1. To define the following terms: *antigen, antibody, epitope, precipitin line,* and *serum.*

2. To distinguish between antigens and antibodies.

3. To learn how the following serological tests are performed: direct fluorescent antibody technique, Ouchterlony technique (double diffusion), enzyme-linked immunosorbent assay and Western blotting technique.

4. To understand the specificity that antigens and antibodies have for each other.

5. To relate non-specific binding to false positive results.

6. To distinguish between positive and negative controls.

7. To compare and contrast the ELISA and Western blotting technique.

The study of immunology is a complex and often abstract endeavor. The key aspects are chemical in nature and therefore difficult to visualize. A number of chemical techniques have been developed to visually represent antibodies and antigens present in the **serum,** the fluid portion of the blood with the clotting factors removed. The study and use of these techniques is referred to as **serology.** These tests are performed *in vitro,* outside of the body, and are primarily used as diagnostic tools to detect disease. Other applications include pregnancy testing and drug testing. These immunological techniques depend upon the principle that an antibody binds only to specific corresponding antigens. The tests are relatively expensive to perform, so this computer simulation will allow you to perform them without the sometimes cost-prohibitive supplies.

Antigens and Antibodies

Antigens are by definition antibody generators. They include proteins, polysaccharides, and various small molecules that stimulate antibody production. Antigens are often molecules that are described as **"non-self,"** or foreign, to the body. However, there are also "self-antigens" that act as identifier tags, such as the proteins found on the surface of red blood cells. Most often, antigens are a portion of an infectious agent such as a bacterium or a virus, and the antibodies that are produced are the body's response to the presence of the infectious agent.

Antigens are often large, with multiple antigenic sites. We refer to these sites as **antigenic determinants,** or **epitopes.** The antibody has a corresponding antigen binding site that has a "lock and key" recognition for the epitope on the antigen. All of the activities presented in this module take advantage of antigen-antibody specificity. They include direct fluorescent antibody technique, Ouchterlony technique, ELISA (enzyme-linked immunosorbent assay), and Western blotting technique.

Positive and Negative Controls

The "lock and key" recognition that antigen and antibody have for each other is much like the specificity that an enzyme and its substrate have for one another. However, with antigen and antibody **non-specific binding** is sometimes possible. For this reason, a number of washing steps to remove any non-specific binding that may have occurred are a common theme in the following experiments. In addition, you will also use **positive and negative controls** to ensure that the test is working accurately. Positive controls include a substance that is known to react positively, thus giving you a standard on which to base your results. Negative controls include substances that should not react. A positive result with a negative control is a "false positive," which would invalidate all other results. Likewise a negative result with a positive control is a "false negative," which would also invalidate your results.

Direct Fluorescent Antibody Technique

The direct fluorescent antibody technique uses antibodies to directly detect the presence of antigen. These antibodies have a fluorescent dye molecule attached to them that acts as a visual signal for a positive result. The antigens that are typically tested for are from infectious agents such as bacteria and viruses. In this experiment you will test for the presence of *Chlamydia trachomatis,* a bacterium that invades the cells of its host, by using fluorescently labeled antibodies to detect the presence of the bacterium. *Chlamydia trachomatis* is an important infectious agent because is causes a sexually transmitted disease known as Chlamydia. If this disease is left untreated it can lead to sterility in men and women.

In this experiment you will test three patients for the Chlamydia infection. The specimen collected from each patient is an epithelial scraping from either the male urethra or the cervix of the uterus. *Chlamydia trachomatis* is an obligate intracellular bacterium, which means that it can only survive inside a host cell. The life cycle of the bacterium has two cellular types. The infectious cell type is the small, dense **elementary body** that is capable of attaching to the host cell. The **reticulate body** is a larger, less dense cell that divides actively, also referred to as the vegetative form. The life cycle of Chlamydia begins when the elementary body enters the host cell and continues as the reticulate body divides and the elementary body releases to infect other cells. The elementary bodies are measured by reacting antigen-specific antibodies to infected cells. The antigen-specific antibodies' fluorescent dye makes the complex detectable. The sample is viewed with a fluorescent microscope. The presence of ten or more elementary bodies in a field of view with a diameter of 5 millimeters is considered a positive result. The elementary bodies will be stained green inside red host cells.

Choose **Serological Testing** from the main menu. The opening screen of the **Direct Fluorescent Antibody** lab will appear in a few seconds (Figure 12.1). Use the **Balloons On/Off** feature from the **Help** menu to familiarize yourself with the lab equipment.

When you begin the simulation, there will be a shelf at the top of the screen that stores the reagents that you will use for this activity. At the far left is *95% ethyl alcohol* that is used as a fixing agent when preparing specimens for microscopy. The bottle labeled *Chlamydia F.A.* contains the *fluorescently-labeled antibodies* that are specific for the Chlamydia antigen. The *F.A. Mounting* bottle contains a special fixative that you will use to preserve the final specimen. The *PBS squirt bottle* is filled with phosphate-buffered saline to remove any excess antibodies that could bind non-specifically and lead to erroneous results. The *F.A. Buffer* is an additional buffer that is designed to remove excess ethyl alcohol after the fixing step. Near the middle of the shelf is a stack of *Petri dishes* that you will use to house the slides and keep them moist during the incubation step. Moving to the right, there is a stack of glass *microscope slides* to prepare patient samples and controls. In the next container are *cotton-tipped applicators* to apply the Chlamydia-fluorescent antibodies to the slide. Next, there's a stack of *filter paper* that has been moistened with F.A. buffer. The filter paper will keep the slides moist during the incubation step. Finally, on the far right are bottles containing the *patient samples*, labeled *A*, *B*, and *C*, and the *positive and negative controls*, labeled + and −.

Below on the left is the *fluorescent microscope* to magnify and observe the final preparation. The *incubator* is on the far right with a timer just to the left. The incubator will automatically open when it is needed. Lower on the screen is the workbench where the microscope slides will be placed along with the Petri dishes. On the bottom is a red biohazard bag for contaminated materials.

Once the samples have been prepared and viewed in the microscope, you will count the number of elementary bodies and record the results in Chart 1 on the next page.

Figure 12.1 Opening screen of Direct Fluorescent Antibody lab.

Activity 1:
Using Direct Fluorescent Antibody Technique to Test for Chlamydia

1. Individually click and drag five slides to the table.

2. The patient samples have been suspended in a small amount of buffer and placed in dropper bottles for ease of dispensing in this simulation. Click on the cap of patient sample **A** to grab the dropper. Drag the dropper over to the first slide. Release the mouse and the sample will dispense. The dropper will return to the bottle.

3. Repeat this process for the remaining patient samples and the positive and negative controls.

4. Click on the dropper cap of the 95% ethyl alcohol and drag the dropper over to the first slide. Release the mouse and three drops of ethyl alcohol will dispense onto each slide.

5. Set the timer for 5 minutes (compressed time) by pressing the (+) button and selecting **Start.** The ethyl alcohol will fix the sample to the slide and prevent the sample from being washed off in the subsequent washing steps.

6. Click on the squirt bottle labeled **F.A.** (Fluorescent Antibody) **Buffer** and drag it over to the first slide. The squirt bottle will rinse all five slides and remove excess ethyl alcohol.

7. Click on the wooden handle of an applicator stick. Move it over to the bottle labeled **Chlamydia F.A.** and release the mouse to soak its cotton tip with antibodies that are specific for Chlamydia and labeled with a fluorescent tag.

8. Click and drag the applicator over to the first slide. Release the mouse to apply the Chlamydia fluorescent antibody to the slide. The applicator will automatically be disposed of in the biohazard bag.

9. Repeat steps 7 and 8 for the remaining slides.

10. Click and drag all five Petri dishes over to the table.

11. A piece of filter paper will be placed in each Petri dish. The filter paper has been moistened with F.A. buffer and will keep the samples from drying out during the incubation step that follows.

12. Click on each slide and drag it over to its Petri dish. Release and the slide will enter the dish and the lid will close.

13. After the last slide is added to the Petri dish, the Petri dishes will be automatically loaded into the incubator.

14. Use the plus (+) button to set the timer to 20 minutes, then select start. During incubation, the antibodies will react with the corresponding antigens that may be present in the sample.

15. The Petri dishes will automatically be removed from the incubator when the time is complete. Click on the squirt bottle of **PBS** (Phosphate Buffered Saline) and drag it to the first Petri dish. It will automatically squirt and rinse each sample to wash off excess antibodies and prevent non-specific binding of the antigen and antibody. The timer will count down 10 minutes for a thorough washing.

16. Click on the first Petri dish to open the dish and remove the slide. Repeat the process for each dish.

17. Click on each Petri dish and drag it to the biohazardous waste receptacle.

18. Click on the dropper for the **F.A. Mounting** media and drag it to the first slide. Release the mouse and the dropper will dispense. Click on the dropper to move it to each slide to mount the sample to the slide.

19. Click on a slide and drag it to the fluorescent microscope. Count the number of elementary bodies and record it in Chart 1 below. Recall that the elementary bodies stain green.

20. After recording the results for a slide, drop it into the biohazard bag for disposal. Complete the chart by repeating these steps for each slide. Then use your results to answer the questions below.

Which patient(s) would be considered positive for Chlamydia?

_____

_____

Are we testing for the presence of antigen or antibody in the patient samples?

_____

Did the controls give the expected results? Explain your answer.

_____

_____

_____

_____

Describe the significance of the washing steps.

_____

_____

_____

_____

Chart 1	Direct Fluorescent Antibody Results
Sample	**Number of Elementary Bodies**
Patient A	
Patient B	
Patient C	
Positive control	
Negative control	

Ouchterlony Technique

Ouchterlony technique is also known as double diffusion. In this technique, antigen and antibody diffuse toward each other in a semi-solid medium made up of clear, clarified agar. When the antigen and antibody are in optimal proportions, cross-linking of the antigen and antibody occurs, forming an insoluble precipitate called a **precipitin line.** These lines can then be used to visually identify and look for similarities between antigens. If optimum proportions have not been met—for example, if there is excess antigen or excess antibody—then no visible precipitate will form. This technique provides easily visible evidence of the binding between antigen and antibody, and sophisticated equipment is not needed to observe the antigen-antibody reaction.

The Ouchterlony technique is designed to determine if antigens are identical, related, or unrelated. Antigens that are related may have some but not all antigenic determinants in common. Antigens are said to have **identity** if they are identical. In the case of identity, precipitin lines diffuse into each other to completely fuse and form an arc. Antigens can also have **partial identity** if they are similar or if they are related. In the case of partial identity, a spur pointing toward the more similar antigen forms in addition to the arc. Antigens that have no similarities or are unrelated have a relationship

referred to as **non-identity.** In this case the lines intersect to form two spurs that resemble an "X."

In Ouchterlony technique, holes are punched into the agar to form wells. The wells are then loaded with either antigen or antibody, which are allowed to diffuse toward each other. Often the same antigen is placed in adjacent wells to assess the purity of an antigen preparation. In this case a smooth arc with no spurs should be seen, as the antigens are identical. Multiple antibodies can also be placed in a center well. The antibodies will diffuse out in all directions and react with the antigens that are placed in the surrounding wells. In this simulation, you will use human and bovine albumin as the antigens, and the antibodies will be made in goats against albumin from either humans or cows (bovine). The goals are to identify an unknown antigen and to observe the patterns produced by the various relationships: identity, partial identity, and non-identity.

From the **Experiment** menu, select **Ouchterlony Double Diffusion**. You will see the opening screen for the Ouchterlony Technique lab (Figure 12.2). Use the **Balloons On/Off** feature from the **Help** menu to familiarize yourself with the equipment on the screen.

In the upper left area of the screen there are several dropper bottles containing either antibodies or antigen. Starting from the far left, the bottle labeled *Goat A-H,* for *goat anti-human albumin,* contains antibodies made in a goat against human albumin. The next bottle is labeled *Goat A-B,* for *goat anti-bovine*

Figure 12.2   Opening screen of the Ouchterlony Technique lab.

albumin, and contains antibodies made in a goat against bovine albumin. The next three bottles contain various antigens: *BSA (bovine serum albumin), HSA (human serum albumin)* and an *unknown antigen.*

Below the top shelf, there is a stack of *Petri dishes* that contain clear agar that has been clarified to remove substances that could inhibit the diffusion. Slightly below is a work bench where you will set up the reactions in the Petri dishes. On the far right is a *well cutter* that will punch holes in the agar.

Just below the well cutter is a timer to time the diffusion process. When the time has elapsed and the diffusion has progressed, you will record your results in Chart 2 below.

Activity 2:
Comparing Samples with Ouchterlony Double Diffusion

1. Click and drag a Petri dish over to the workbench. The lid will open to reveal an enlarged view of the inside of the Petri dish.

2. Click and drag the well cutter to the enlarged view of the Petri dish. Punch a hole in the middle of the Petri dish by releasing the mouse button. Now punch four more holes around the center hole.

3. After the fifth well is punched, the well cutter will return to the shelf and the wells will be labeled 1 through 5.

4. Click on the dropper of the bottle labeled **Goat A-H.** This bottle contains the goat anti-human albumin, which is an anti-serum containing antibodies produced by goats against human albumin. Drag the dropper to well 1 and fill it with a sample.

5. Repeat this procedure for the bottle labeled **Goat A-B,** which contains the goat anti-bovine albumin. This is an anti-serum containing antibodies produced by goats against bovine (cow) albumin. Release the mouse to also add this solution to well 1.

6. Click on the dropper for the bottle labeled **BSA,** which contains bovine serum albumin. Drag the dropper over to well 2 and release to dispense BSA.

7. Dispense BSA into well 3 using the same procedure as step 6.

Chart 2	Ouchterlony Double Diffusion Results
Wells	**Identity**
2 and 5	
2 and 3	
3 and 4	
4 and 5	

8. Click on the dropper of the bottle labeled **HSA,** which contains human serum albumin. Drag the dropper over to well 4 and release to dispense HSA.

9. Click on the dropper for the bottle labeled **Unknown** and drag it over to well 5. Release the mouse to dispense the unknown into well 5.

10. Use the plus (**+**) button to set the timer to 16 hours. Click on the **Start** button to start the timer. The antigen and antibodies will diffuse toward each other and form a precipitate detected as a precipitin line.

Examine the precipitin lines that formed. Fill out Chart 2 by determining if each pair has identity, partial identity, or non-identity.

What is the identity of the unknown? How do you know this?

_____

_____

_____

Which components are the antigens in this experiment?

_____

_____

What role does albumin usually play in serum?

_____

_____

_____

Why do you think the agar needs to be clear and clarified?

_____

_____

_____

Enzyme-Linked Immunosorbent Assay (ELISA)

ELISA is an acronym for **enzyme-linked immunosorbent assay.** The assay is considered enzyme-linked because an enzyme is chemically linked to an antibody in both the direct and indirect versions of the test. Immunosorbent refers to the fact that either antigens or antibodies are being adsorbed (stuck) to plastic. ELISA can test for the presence of antigen or antibody. If the test is designed to detect an antigen or antigens, it is a **direct ELISA** because it is directly looking for the foreign substance. An **indirect ELISA** is designed to detect antibodies that the patient has made against the antigen. **Seroconversion** occurs when a patient goes from testing negative for a specific antibody to testing positive for the same antibody.

In the direct ELISA, the 96-well-microtiter plate is coated with homologous antibodies made against the antigen of interest. The patient serum sample is added to the plate to test for the presence of the antigen that binds to the antibody coating on the plate. Then a secondary antibody is added. If the antigen is present, a "sandwich" of antibody, antigen, and secondary antibody will form. The secondary antibody is chemically linked to an enzyme. When the substrate is added, the enzyme converts the substrate from a colorless compound to a colored compound. The amount of color produced will be proportional to the amount of antigen present and thus determines if the patient is positive for the antigen.

In the indirect ELISA, the 96-well-microtiter plate is coated with antigens. The large number of wells makes it easy to test many samples at a time. The patient serum sample is added to test for the presence of antibodies that bind to the antigens on the plate. The secondary antibody that is added has an enzyme linked to it that binds to the **constant region** of the primary antibody if it is present in the patient sample. The constant region of an antibody has the same sequence of amino acids within a class of antibodies, e.g., IgG would have the same constant region. The **variable region** of an antibody provides the diversity of antibodies and is the site to which the antigen binds. The configuration that forms in the indirect ELISA is antigen, antibody, and secondary antibody. Just as in

the direct ELISA, the addition of substrate is used to determine if the sample is positive for the presence of antibody.

In this simulation, you will use the indirect ELISA to test for the presence of antibodies made against Human Immunodeficiency Virus (HIV). You will use positive and negative controls to verify the results.

From the **Experiment** menu, select **Indirect ELISA**. You will see the opening screen for the lab (Figure 12.3). Use the **Balloons On/Off** feature from the **Help** menu to familiarize yourself with the equipment on the screen.

At the left hand corner of the screen in an open cabinet are two *pipettors* that will be used to dispense small volumes. The pipettor on the left is a *multi-channel pipettor* that can dispense eight samples at once, and the other is a *100 μl pipettor*. In the same cabinet is a *96-well microtiter plate,* a plastic tray that has 12 wells across and 8 wells down. The closed cabinet to the right contains the patient samples and controls that will be used later in the lab. It will automatically open when necessary. On the far right is a *microtiter plate reader* that will detect the optical density of the samples after the reaction has occurred. Just below the plate reader is a *pipette tip dispenser* that contains single-use, disposable pipette tips. The *Washing Buffer* will be used to remove excess reagents and reduce non-specific binding. The *Antigens* bottle contains the HIV antigens that will be adsorbed (stuck)

Figure 12.3   Opening screen of the Enzyme-Linked Immunosorbent Assay (ELISA) lab.

to the plastic of the microtiter plate. The *Developing Buffer* bottle contains the secondary antibody to which the enzyme is conjugated. The *Substrates* bottle contains the substrates that the enzyme converts from a colorless compound to a colored compound.

At the lower left of the screen is a *sink* that will be used to remove liquids from the microtiter plate. Next to the sink is a *blotter* that will be used to remove the last amount of liquid from the wells of the microtiter plate. Next to the blotter is the workbench. Below the workbench is the *data table* for recording the optical density of each sample. In the lower right corner is a *biohazard bag* for the disposal of biohazardous waste.

Activity 3
Using Indirect ELISA to Test for HIV

1. Click on the 96-well-microtiter plate and hold down the mouse button to drag it over to the workbench. Release the button to drop it there.

2. Move the multi-channel pipettor to the pipette tip dispenser. Release the mouse to insert the tips.

3. Bring the multi-channel pipettor to the bottle labeled antigens. Release the mouse to add the antigen solution for dispensing.

4. Position the multi-channel pipettor directly over the 96-well-microtiter plate. Release the mouse to dispense the liquid into the wells. You are filling up one row of the plate.

5. Click and drag the multi-channel pipettor to the biohazard bin for removal and disposal of the tips.

6. Using the plus (+) button, set the timer to 14 hours. Click on the **Start** button to start the timer.

7. After the simulated 14 hours have passed, click on the bottle of **Washing Buffer** and drag it over to the 96-well-microtiter plate. Release the mouse and the solution will squirt into the tray. The washing buffer is used to remove excess antigens that are not adsorbed (stuck) to the plate.

8. Click on the 96-well-microtiter plate and drag it to the sink. Release the mouse and the contents of the tray will be dumped into the sink.

9. Repeat the washing steps twice by repeating steps 7 and 8 twice.

10. Click and drag the 96-well-microtiter plate over to the blotter. Release the mouse and the plate will be pressed to the surface of the blotter to remove the last amount of liquid from the wells.

11. Click on the 100μl pipettor and drag it over to the tip dispenser. Release the mouse to place a tip onto the pipettor.

12. Click and drag the 100μl pipettor over to the positive control bottle, labeled **+**. Release the mouse and the sample will be drawn up into the pipette tip.

13. Click and drag the 100μl pipettor over to the 96-well-microtiter plate. Release the mouse and the sample will be dispensed into the wells of the plate. The tip will automatically be removed and disposed of in the biohazardous waste.

14. Repeat the process for each of the samples.

15. An enlargement of the wells will appear to show you where you placed the samples. Click on the **(X)** to close the pop-up window.

16. Set the timer for 1 hour using the (+) button. Click on the **Start** button to start the timer. This process will allow the antigens to react with each of the samples.

17. After the time has elapsed, click on the **Washing Buffer** and drag it over to the 96-well-microtiter plate. Release the mouse and the solution will squirt into the tray. The washing buffer is used to remove any non-specific binding that may have occurred.

18. Click on the 96-well-microtiter plate and drag it to the sink. Release the mouse and the contents of the tray will be dumped into the sink.

19. Repeat the washing steps twice by repeating steps 17 and 18 twice.

20. Click and drag the 96-well-microtiter plate over to the blotter. Release the mouse and the plate will be pressed to the surface of the blotter to remove the last amount of liquid from the wells.

21. Click on the multi-channel pipettor and drag it to the tip dispenser. Release the mouse to attach the tips to the multi-channel pipettor.

22. Click and drag the multi-channel pipettor to the developing buffer. Release the mouse and the buffer will be drawn up into the tips. The developing buffer contains the conjugated secondary antibody.

23. Click on the multi-channel pipettor and drag it to the 96-well-microtiter plate. Release the mouse and the solution will dispense into the wells. Click on the multi-channel pipettor and drag it to the biohazardous waste.

24. Set the timer for 1 hour, and then press **Start**. This will allow the conjugated secondary antibody to bind to the primary antibody if it is present in the sample.

25. Click on the multi-channel pipettor and drag it to the tip dispenser. Release the mouse to attach tips to the pipettor.

26. Click and drag the multi-channel pipettor to the **Substrate** bottle. Release the mouse and the solution will be drawn up into the tips.

27. Click on the multi-channel pipettor and drag it to the 96-well-microtiter plate. The substrate will be added to the wells.

28. Click on the multi-channel pipettor and drag it to the biohazardous waste. Release the mouse to release the tips.

29. An enlargement of the wells will appear. The development will progress over time. Click on a well and the optical density will appear in the window of the microtiter plate reader. Click on the **Record** button to record the optical density in the Data Table, then record the test results in Chart 3 using the following guidelines:

- A result of <0.300 is read as negative for HIV-1.

- A result of 0.300 – 0.499 is read as indeterminate, need to retest.

- A result of >0.500 is read as positive for HIV-1.

Chart 3	Indirect ELISA Results	
Sample	**Optical Density**	**HIV Test Result**
Patient A		
Patient B		
Patient C		
Positive control		
Negative control		

Which patient(s) would be considered positive for HIV?

_____

_____

_____

Are we testing for the presence of antigen or antibody in the patient samples?

_____

_____

_____

What key substance is present in the "Developing Buffer"?

_____

_____

_____

What does seroconversion mean? Which patient would be positive for seroconversion?

_____ ■

Western Blotting Technique

Southern blotting was developed by Ed Southern in 1975 to identify DNA. A variation of this technique, developed to identify RNA, was named Northern blotting, thus continuing the directional theme. Western blotting, another variation that identifies proteins, is named following the same tradition.

The full procedure involves using an electrical current to separate proteins on the basis of their size and charge. This technique uses **gel electrophoresis** to separate the proteins in a gel matrix. Because the resulting gel is fragile and would be difficult to use in further tests, the proteins are then transferred to a **nitrocellulose membrane.** The original Western blot technique used blotting to transfer the proteins, but now electricity is also used for the transfer of the proteins to nitrocellulose strips. These strips are commercially available, which eliminates the need for the electrophoresis and transfer equipment. This simulation with pick up the procedure with the HIV (Human Immunodeficiency Virus) antigens already transferred to nitrocellulose and cut into strips.

Western blotting is also known as **immunoblotting.** This is because the proteins that are transferred, or blotted, onto the membrane are later treated with antibodies. In a manner similar to the ELISA technique, the secondary antibodies have an enzyme attached to them that allows the use of color to detect a particular protein. The main difference is that the ELISA technique uses a well that corresponds to a mixture of antigens, whereas the Western blot has a discrete protein band that represents the specific antigen that the antibody is recognizing.

The initial test for HIV is the ELISA, which is less expensive and easier to perform than the Western blot. The Western blot is used as a confirmatory, test for a positive ELISA because the ELISA is prone to false positive results. The bands from a positive Western blot are from antibodies binding to specific proteins and glycoproteins from the human immunodeficiency virus. A positive result from the Western blot is determined by the presence of particular protein bands.

From the **Experiment** menu, select **Western Blot.** You will see the opening screen for the lab (Figure 12.4). Use the **Balloons On/Off** feature from the **Help** menu to familiarize yourself with the equipment on the screen.

At the left there is a shelf that contains *Washing Buffer* that will be used to wash away excess reagents and reduce non-specific binding. The bottle labeled *Developing Buffer* contains the secondary antibody to which the enzyme alkaline phosphatase is conjugated. The *Substrates* in the next bottle are tetramethyl benzidine and hydrogen peroxide, the specific reactants that are used by the alkaline phosphatase enzyme found in the developing buffer. The right hand shelf has the three patient samples (*A*, *B*, and *C*) and the *positive and negative controls.* Below this shelf is a stack of *nitrocellulose strips* that have been prepared with the HIV antigens, and a stack of *troughs* that will be used to house the nitrocellulose strips during the reaction. These strips are commercially available. Usually, they are stored in a plastic bag with a solution to keep them from drying out. However, for the ease of the simulation they will be kept out of the bag.

Moving down the screen, there is a *rocking apparatus* that will be used to gently mix the samples. The timer for the rocking apparatus is just below the apparatus. Just to the right is a workbench with a *tray* that will be used to transfer the troughs to the rocking apparatus. Below the workbench is the *data table.* The protein bands present will be recorded by clicking **Record Data** for each sample. In the far right corner is a *biohazard bag* used to dispose of the contaminated materials.

Figure 12.4 Opening screen of the Western Blot lab.

Activity 4:
Using Western Blot Strips to Detect Anti-HIV Antibodies

1. Click a trough from the shelf to place it on the tray on the workbench. Repeat this process until there are five troughs on the tray.

2. Click on the stack of nitrocellulose strips, then release the mouse and a strip will drop into the trough. Repeat this process to place a nitrocellulose strip in each trough.

3. Click on the dropper cap of the patient sample labeled **A**. The dropper will appear. Then drag the dropper over to the first trough. Release the mouse and the sample will dispense. The dropper will return to the bottle. This step adds the anti-serum from patient **A** to the nitrocellulose strip.

4. Repeat this step for the remaining anti-sera: patient **B** sample, patient **C** sample, and the positive and negative controls.

5. Click on the tray that is holding the five troughs and drag it to the rocking apparatus.

6. Set the timer for 60 minutes using the plus (**+**) button, and then click **Start.** The gentle rocking action will allow the antibodies to react with the antigens bound to the nitrocellulose.

7. When the time has elapsed, click on the tray and drag it back to the workbench.

8. Click on the first trough and drag it to the biohazardous waste container. The trough will tilt and drain off the liquid. Repeat this process for each trough.

9. Click on the squirt bottle of **Washing Buffer** and drag it over to the first trough. The bottle will add washing buffer to each trough. Then each trough will be drained into the biohazardous waste container.

10. Repeat the washing steps two more times by adding washing buffer to the first trough. The washing and rinsing steps will automatically repeat each time. These washing steps are performed to remove any non-specific binding of antibodies that may have occurred.

11. Click on the dropper bottle of **Developing Buffer** and add this solution to the first trough by dragging the dropper to the trough and releasing the mouse. Move the dropper over to the next trough to add developing buffer to each trough.

12. Click on the tray and drag it to the rocking apparatus. Set the timer for 60 minutes using the (**+**) button, and then press **Start.** This will allow the conjugated secondary antibody to bind to the primary antibody if it is present in the sample.

13. When the time has elapsed, click on the tray and drag it back to the workbench.

14. Click on the first trough and drag it to the biohazardous waste container. The trough will tilt and drain off the liquid. Repeat this process for each trough.

15. Click on the squirt bottle of **Washing Buffer** and drag it over to the first trough. The bottle will add washing buffer to each trough as it passes over the trough. Each trough will be drained into the biohazardous waste container.

16. Repeat the washing steps two more times by adding washing buffer to the first trough. The washing and rinsing steps will automatically repeat each time. These washing steps are performed to remove any non-specific binding of secondary conjugated antibodies. Excess secondary conjugated antibody could react erroneously with substrate and give a false positive result.

17. Click on the dropper for the bottle labeled **Substrates.** Then drag the dropper over to the first trough and release the mouse button to dispense the substrates (tetramethyl benzidine and hydrogen peroxide) into the trough. Move the dropper over to the next trough and repeat until the substrates have been added to each trough. The substrates are the chemicals that are being changed by the enzyme that is linked to the antibody.

18. Click on the tray and drag it to the rocking apparatus.

19. Set the timer for 10 minutes using the (+) button. Click the **Start** button to start the timer.

20. Click on the tray and drag it to the workbench. Click on the nitrocellulose strip inside the trough to visualize each result. Then click **Record Data** to enter the results in the data table. The bands are a result of the enzyme that is linked to the secondary antibody reacting with the substrates and creating the color.

21. Use the criteria below to report an overall result for the patient or control samples. The antigens that are present on the nitrocellulose strips are the following proteins from HIV:

Abbreviation	Description
gp 160	Glycoprotein 160, a viral envelope precursor
gp 120	Glycoprotein 120, a viral envelope protein that binds to CD4
p55	A precursor to the viral core protein p24
gp41	A final envelope protein
p31	Reverse transcriptase
p24	Viral core protein

The criteria for reporting a positive result varies slightly from agency to agency. The Centers for Disease Control and Prevention recommend the following criteria that we will use for this simulation.

Observation	Reported Result
No bands are present.	Negative
Either p31 or p24 are present *and* gp 160 or gp 120 are present.	Positive
Bands are present, but they do not match the criteria for a positive result.	Indeterminate

Patients that are deemed indeterminate after multiple testing should be monitored and tested again at a later date.

Fill in Chart 4 using the information in the data table to determine the reported results for each patient and control sample.

What are bound to the nitrocellulose initially, antigens or antibodies?

_____

_____

_____

Chart 4	Western Blot Results
Sample	**Reported Result**
Patient A	
Patient B	
Patient C	
Positive control	
Negative control	

Compare and contrast the indirect ELISA and the Western blot technique.

_____

_____

_____

_____

_____

_____

Which test do you think would be more specific, the indirect ELISA or the Western blot technique? Why?

_____

_____

_____

_____

Histology Tutorial

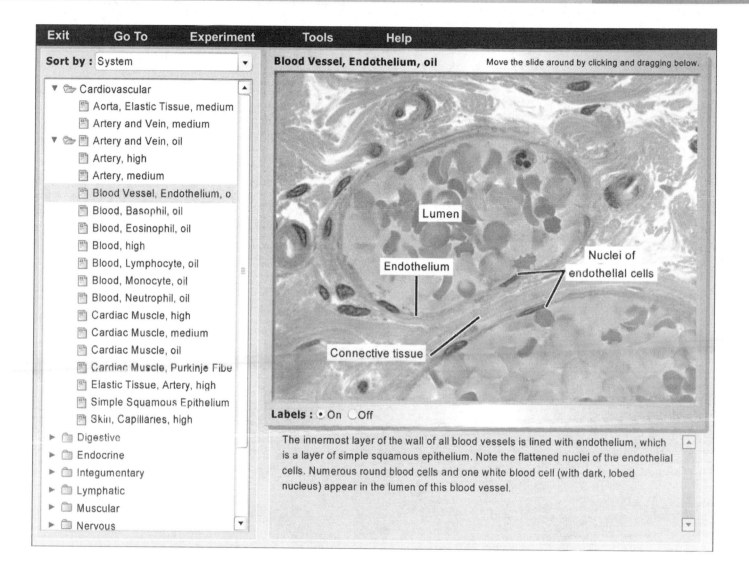

Blood Vessel, Endothelium, oil — Move the slide around by clicking and dragging below.

Labels : ● On ○ Off

The innermost layer of the wall of all blood vessels is lined with endothelium, which is a layer of simple squamous epithelium. Note the flattened nuclei of the endothelial cells. Numerous round blood cells and one white blood cell (with dark, lobed nucleus) appear in the lumen of this blood vessel.

---

xamining a specimen using a microscope accomplishes two goals: first, it gives you an understanding of the cellular organization of tissues, and second —perhaps even more importantly—it hones your observational skills. Because developing these skills is crucial in the understanding and eventual mastery of the scientific method, using this histology tutorial is not intended as a substitute for using the microscope. Instead, use it to gain an overall appreciation of the specimens and then make your own observations using your microscope.

The Histology Tutorial can be used independently of this lab manual to explore the different tissue types found in the human body. Or, it can be used in conjunction with the printed worksheets found in the Histology Review Supplement on page 123, for a review of histology slides specific to topics covered in the PhysioEx lab simulations.

To begin, select **Histology Tutorial** from the main menu. The opening screen should appear after a few seconds. There are four main components of the tutorial. The *Sort by* drop down menu is located at the top left. After you select a sorting option, the *slide menu* below will display all the folders and slide listings that are available. The *image viewer* is located at the top right with the *description box* directly below it.

Sorting and Locating Slides

You can search for slides by selecting any of the four sorting options from the *Sort by* drop down menu. Click on the white menu bar to select from the following sorting options:

- **A-Z** Organizes slides alphabetically by title. Contains all of the slide listings in the tutorial.
- **System** Organizes slides into folders based on the body system they represent.
- **Tissue Type** Organizes slides into folders based on the tissue type(s) they represent.
- **Histology Review** Calls up the images used in the Histology Review Supplement section of this lab manual. See page 123 for more information.

Certain histology images demonstrate more than one system or tissue type; therefore, an image might be found in multiple locations with different titles, labels and descriptions, depending on the categories it is listed under.

All slide listings include magnification information at the end of the title. Because the exact magnification is variable depending on screen resolution, we have provided approximate magnifications instead:

- **low** originally photographed at **40X**
- **medium** originally photographed at **100X**
- **high** originally photographed at **400X**
- **oil (immersion)** originally photographed at **1000X**

Viewing Slides and Labels

Click on any listing in the *slide menu* to call up an image and description in the viewing area. The image may take a few seconds to load if you are using the web version. You can move the slide around in the viewer by clicking and dragging directly on the image.

You can show or hide the labels at any time by selecting the **On** or **Off** buttons in the *Labels* menu below the viewer. If a label appears to be out of the viewing area, keep in mind that you can see more of the image by clicking and dragging it in the *image viewer*.

Histology
Review
Supplement

The slides in this section are designed to provide a basic histology review related to topics introduced in the PhysioEx lab simulations and in your anatomy and physiology textbook.

From the PhysioEx main menu, select **Histology Tutorial.** The opening screen should appear after a few seconds. The *Sort by* menu is located at the top left. Click on the white drop-down menu and select "Histology Review" from the list. You will note that the slides in the histology module are grouped in the following folders:

Skeletal muscle slides

Nervous tissue slides

Endocrine tissue slides

Cardiovascular tissue slides

Respiratory tissue slides

Digestive tissue slides

Renal tissue slides

Select the group of slides you wish to view, and then refer to the relevant worksheet in this section for a step-by-step tutorial. For example, if you would like to review the skeletal muscle slides, click on the **Skeletal muscle slides** folder, and then turn to the next page of this lab manual for the worksheet entitled Skeletal Muscle Tissue Review to begin your review. You will have the option of viewing slides with or without labels by clicking the **On/Off** buttons at the bottom left of the viewer.

Since the slides in this module have been selected for their relevance to topics covered in the PhysioEx lab simulation, it is recommended that you complete the worksheets along with a related PhysioEx lab. For example, you might complete the Skeletal Muscle Tissue worksheet right before or after your instructor assigns you Exercise 2, the PhysioEx lab simulation on Skeletal Muscle Physiology.

For additional histology review, turn to page 121.

Skeletal Muscle Tissue Review

From the PhysioEx main menu, select **Histology Review Supplement.** When the screen comes up, click **Select an Image Group.** From Group Listing, click **Skeletal muscle slides.** To view slides without labels, click the **Labels Off** button at the bottom right of the monitor.

Click slide 1.
Skeletal muscle is composed of extremely large, cylindrical multinucleated cells called **myofibers.** The nuclei of the skeletal muscle cell (**myonuclei**) are located peripherally just subjacent to the muscle cell plasmalemma (sarcolemma). The interior of the cell is literally filled with an assembly of contractile proteins (myofilaments) arranged in a specific overlapping pattern oriented parallel to the long axis of the cell.

Click slides 2, 3.
Sarcomeres are the functional units of skeletal muscle. The organization of contractile proteins into a regular end-to-end repeating pattern of sarcomeres along the length of each cell accounts for the striated, or striped, appearance of skeletal muscle in longitudinal section.

Click slide 4.
The **smooth endoplasmic reticulum** (sarcoplasmic reticulum), modified into an extensive network of membranous channels that store, release, and take up the calcium necessary for contraction, also functions to further organize the myofilaments inside the cell into cylindrical bundles called myofibrils. The **stippled appearance of the cytoplasm** in cells cut in cross section represents the internal organization of myofilaments bundled into myofibrils by the membranous sarcoplasmic reticulum.

What is the functional unit of contraction in skeletal muscle?

_____

What are the two principal contractile proteins that compose the functional unit of contraction?

_____

What is the specific relationship of the functional unit of contraction to the striated appearance of a skeletal muscle fiber?

_____

_____

Click slide 5.
The neural stimulus for contraction arises from the **axon** of a motor neuron whose axon terminal comes into close apposition to the muscle cell sarcolemma.

Would you characterize skeletal muscle as voluntary or involuntary?

_____

Name the site of close juxtaposition of an axon terminal with the muscle cell plasmalemma.

_____

Skeletal muscle also has an extensive connective tissue component that, in addition to conducting blood vessels and nerves, becomes continuous with the connective tissue of its tendon. The tendon in turn is directly continuous with the connective tissue covering (the periosteum) of the adjacent bone. This connective tissue continuity from muscle to tendon to bone is the basis for movement of the musculoskeletal system.

What is the name of the loose areolar connective tissue covering of an individual muscle fiber?

_____

The perimysium is a collagenous connective tissue layer that groups several muscle fibers together into bundles called

_____.

Which connective tissue layer surrounds the entire muscle and merges with the connective tissue of tendons and aponeuroses?

_____

Nervous Tissue Review

From the PhysioEx main menu, select **Histology Review Supplement.** When the screen comes up, click **Select an Image Group.** From Group Listing, click **Nervous tissue slides.** To view slides without labels, click the **Labels Off** button at the bottom right of the monitor.

Nervous tissue is composed of nerve cells (neurons) and a variety of support cells.

Click slide 1.
Each nerve cell consists of a **cell body** (perikaryon) and one or more **cellular processes** (axon and dendrites) extending from it. The cell body contains the **nucleus,** which is typically pale-staining and round or spherical in shape, and the usual assortment of cytoplasmic organelles. Characteristically, the nucleus features a prominent **nucleolus** often described as resembling the pupil of a bird's eye (**"bird's eye,"** or "owl's eye," nucleolus).

Click slide 2.
The cytoplasm of the cell body is most often granular in appearance due to the presence of darkly stained clumps of ribosomes and rough endoplasmic reticulum (**Nissl bodies/ Nissl substance).** Generally, a single axon arises from the **cell body** at a pale-staining region (axon hillock), devoid of Nissl bodies. The location and number of dendrites arising from the cell body varies greatly.

Axons and dendrites are grouped together in the peripheral nervous system (PNS) to form peripheral nerves.

What is the primary unit of function in nervous tissue?

_____

Name the pale staining region of the cell body from which the axon arises.

_____

The support cells of the nervous system perform extremely important functions including support, protection, insulation, and maintenance and regulation of the microenvironment that surrounds the nerve cells.

Click slides 3, 4.
In the PNS, support cells surround cell bodies (satellite cells) and individual **axons** and **dendrites** (Schwann cells). Schwann cells, in particular, are responsible for wrapping their cell membrane jelly-roll style around axons and dendrites to form an insulating sleeve called the **myelin sheath.**

Click slide 5.
Because Schwann cells are aligned in series and myelinate only a small segment of a single axon, small gaps occur between the myelin sheaths of adjacent contiguous Schwann cells. The gaps, called **nodes of Ranvier,** together with the insulating properties of **myelin,** enhance the speed of conduction of electrical impulses along the length of the axon. Different support cells and myelinating cells are present in the central nervous system (CNS).

What is the general name for all support cells within the CNS?

_____

Name the specific myelinating cell of the CNS.

_____

In the PNS, connective tissue also plays a role in providing support and organization. In fact, the composition and organization of the connective tissue investments of peripheral nerves are similar to those of skeletal muscle.

Click slide 3.
Each individual axon or dendrite is surrounded by a thin and delicate layer of loose connective tissue called the endoneurium (not shown.) The **perineurium,** a slightly thicker layer of loose connective tissue, groups many axons and dendrites together into bundles (fascicles). The outermost **epineurium** surrounds the entire nerve with a thick layer of dense irregular connective tissue, often infiltrated with adipose tissue, that conveys blood and lymphatic vessels to the nerve. There is no connective tissue component within the nervous tissue of the CNS.

What is the relationship of the endoneurium to the myelin sheath?

_____

_____

Endocrine Tissue Review

From the PhysioEx main menu, select **Histology Review Supplement.** When the screen comes up, click **Select an Image Group.** From Group Listing, click **Endocrine tissue slides.** To view slides without labels, click the **Labels Off** button at the bottom right of the monitor.

Thyroid Gland

The thyroid gland regulates metabolism by regulating the secretion of the hormones T_3 (triiodothyronine) and T_4 (thyroxine) into the blood.

Click slide 1.
The gland is composed of fluid-filled (**colloid**) spheres, called **follicles,** formed by a simple epithelium that can be squamous to columnar depending upon the gland's activity. The colloid stored in the follicles is primarily composed of a glycoprotein (thyroglobulin) that is synthesized and secreted by the follicular cells. Under the influence of the pituitary gland, the follicular cells take up the colloid, convert it into T_3 and T_4, and secrete the T_3 and T_4 into an extensive capillary network. A second population of cells, parafollicular (C) cells (not shown), may be found scattered through the follicular epithelium but often are present in the connective tissue between follicles. The pale-staining parafollicular cells secrete the protein hormone calcitonin.

Why is the thyroid gland considered to be an endocrine organ?

What hormone secreted by the pituitary gland controls the synthesis and secretion of T_3 and T_4?

What is the function of calcitonin?

Ovary

The ovary is an organ that serves both an exocrine function in producing eggs (ova) and an endocrine function in secreting the hormones estrogen and progesterone.

Click slide 2.
Grossly, the ovary is divided into a peripherally located **cortex** in which the oocytes (precursors to the ovulated egg) develop and a central **medulla** in which connective tissue surrounds blood vessels, lymphatic vessels and nerves. The oocytes, together with supporting cells (granulosa cells), form the **ovarian follicles** seen in the cortex at various stages of development.

Click slide 3.
As an individual oocyte grows, **granulosa cells** proliferate from a single layer of cuboidal cells that surround the oocyte to a multicellular layer that defines a fluid-filled spherical follicle. In a mature follicle (Graafian follicle), the **granulosa cells** are displaced to the periphery of the fluid-filled

antrum, except for a thin rim of granulosa cells (**corona radiata**) that encircles the **oocyte** and a pedestal of granulosa cells (cumulus oophorus) that attaches the oocyte to the inner wall of the antrum.

Which cells of the ovarian follicle secrete estrogen?

Uterus

Click slides 4, 5, 6.
The uterus is a hollow muscular organ with three major layers: the **endometrium, myometrium,** and either an adventitia or a serosa.

The middle, myometrial layer of the uterine wall is composed of several layers of smooth muscle oriented in different planes.

Click slide 6.
The innermost (nearest the lumen) endometrial layer is further divided functionally into a superficial functional layer (**stratum functionalis**) and a deep basal layer (**stratum basalis).**

Click slide 4.
A simple columnar **epithelium** with both ciliated and nonciliated cells lines the surface of the **endometrium.** The endometrial connective tissue features an abundance of tubular endometrial **glands** that extend from the base to the surface of the layer. During the proliferative phase of the menstrual cycle, shown here, the endometrium becomes thicker as the glands and blood vessels proliferate.

Click slide 5.
In the secretory phase, the **endometrium** and its **glands** and blood vessels are fully expanded.

Click slide 6.
In the menstrual phase, the glands and blood vessels degenerate as the functional layer of the endometrium sloughs away. The deep basal layer (**stratum basalis**) is not sloughed and will regenerate the endometrium during the next proliferative phase.

Which layer of the endometrium is shed during the menstrual phase of the menstrual cycle?

What is the function of the deep basal layer (stratum basalis) of the endometrium?

What composes a serosa?

How does the serosa of the uterus, where present, differ from visceral peritoneum?

Pancreas

The pancreas is both an endocrine and an exocrine gland.

Click slide 7.

The exocrine portion is characterized by glandular **secretory units** (acini) formed by a simple epithelium of triangular or pyramidal cells that encircle a small central lumen. The central lumen is the direct connection to the duct system that conveys the exocrine secretions out of the gland. Scattered among the exocrine secretory units are the pale-staining clusters of cells that compose the endocrine portion of the gland. The cells that form these clusters, called pancreatic islet cells **(islets of Langerhans),** secrete a number of hormones, including insulin and glucagon.

Do the pancreatic islets secrete their hormones into the same duct system used by the exocrine secretory cells?

Cardiovascular Tissue Review

From the PhysioEx main menu, select **Histology Review Supplement.** When the screen comes up, click **Select an Image Group.** From Group Listing, click **Cardiovascular Tissue Slides.** To view slides without labels, click the **Labels Off** button at the bottom right of the monitor.

Heart

The heart is a four-chambered muscular pump. Although its wall can be divided into three distinct histological layers (endocardium, myocardium, and epicardium), the cardiac muscle of the myocardium composes the bulk of the heart wall.

Click slide 1.
Contractile **cardiac muscle cells** (myocytes, myofibers) have the same striated appearance as skeletal muscle, but are branched rather than cylindrical in shape and have one (occasionally two) **nucleus** (myonucleus) rather than many. The cytoplasmic **striations** represent the same organization of myofilaments (sarcomeres) and alignment of sarcomeres as in skeletal muscle, and the mechanism of contraction is the same. The **intercalated disc,** however, is a feature unique to cardiac muscle. The densely stained structure is a complex of intercellular junctions (desmosomes, gap junctions, fasciae adherens) that structurally and functionally link cardiac muscle cells end to end.

A second population of cells in the myocardium composes the noncontractile intrinsic conduction system (nodal system). Although cardiac muscle is autorhythmic, meaning it has the ability to contract involuntarily in the absence of extrinsic innervation provided by the nervous system, it is the intrinsic conduction system that prescribes the rate and orderly sequence of contraction. Extrinsic innervation only modulates the inherent activity.

Click slide 2.
Of the various components of the noncontractile intrinsic conduction system, **Purkinje fibers** are the most readily observed histologically. They are particularly abundant in the ventricular myocardium and are recognized by their very pale-staining cytoplasm and larger diameter.

The connective tissue component of cardiac muscle is relatively sparse and lacks the organization present in skeletal muscle.

Which component of the intercalated disc is a strong intercellular junction that functions to keep cells from being pulled apart during contraction?

_____

_____

What is a functional syncytium?

_____

_____

Which component of the intercalated disc is a junction that provides the intercellular communication required for the myocardium to perform as a functional syncytium?

_____

_____

Blood Vessels

Blood vessels form a system of conduits through which life-sustaining blood is conveyed from the heart to all parts of the body and back to the heart again.

Click slide 3.
Generally, the wall of every vessel is described as being composed of three layers, or *tunics.* The **tunica intima,** or *tunica interna,* a simple squamous endothelium and a small amount of subjacent loose connective tissue, is the innermost layer adjacent to the vessel lumen. Smooth muscle and elastin are the predominant constituents of the middle **tunica media,** and the outermost **tunica adventitia,** or *tunica externa,* is a connective tissue layer of variable thickness that provides support and transmits smaller blood and lymphatic vessels and nerves. The thickness of each tunic varies widely with location and function of the vessel. **Arteries,** subjected to considerable pressure fluctuations, have thicker walls overall, with the tunica media being thicker than the tunica adventitia. **Veins,** in contrast, are subjected to much lower pressures and have thinner walls overall, with the tunica adventitia often outsizing the tunica media. Because thin-walled veins conduct blood back to the heart against gravity, valves (not present in arteries) also are present at intervals to prevent backflow. In capillaries, where exchange occurs between the blood and tissues, the tunica intima alone composes the vessel wall.

The tunica media of the aorta would have a much greater proportion of what type of tissue than a small artery?

_____

In general, which vessel would have a larger lumen, an artery or its corresponding vein?

_____

Why would the tunica media and tunica adventitia not be present in a capillary?

_____

Respiratory Tissue Review

From the PhysioEx main menu, select **Histology Review Supplement.** When the screen comes up, click **Select an Image Group.** From Group Listing, click **Respiratory Tissue Slides.** To view slides without labels, click the **Labels Off** button at the bottom right of the monitor.

The respiratory system serves both to conduct oxygenated air deep into the lungs and to exchange oxygen and carbon dioxide between the air and the blood. The trachea, bronchi, and bronchioles are the part of the system of airways that conduct air into the lungs.

Click slide 2.
The trachea and bronchi are similar in morphology. Their lumens are lined by **pseudostratified columnar ciliated epithelium** with **goblet cells** (respiratory epithelium), underlain by a connective tissue **lamina propria** and a deeper connective tissue submucosa with coiled sero-mucous glands that open onto the surface lining of the airway lumen.

Click slide 1.
Deep to the submucosa are the **hyaline cartilage rings** that add structure to the wall of the airway and prevent its collapse. Peripheral to the cartilage is a connective tissue adventitia. The **sero-mucous glands** are also visible in this slide.

Click slide 3.
The bronchioles, in contrast, are much smaller in diameter with a continuous layer of **smooth muscle** in place of the cartilaginous reinforcements. A gradual decrease in the height of the epithelium to **simple columnar** also occurs as the bronchioles decrease in diameter. Distally the bronchioles give way to the respiratory bronchioles, alveolar ducts, alveolar sacs, and alveoli in which gas exchange occurs. In the respiratory bronchiole, the epithelium becomes simple cuboidal and the continuous smooth muscle layer is interrupted at intervals by the presence of alveoli inserted into the bronchiolar wall.

Click slide 4.
Although some exchange occurs in the respiratory bronchiole, it is within the **alveoli** of the alveolar ducts and **sacs** that the preponderance of gas exchange transpires. Here the walls of the alveoli, devoid of smooth muscle, are reduced in thickness to the thinnest possible juxtaposition of simple squamous alveolar cell to simple squamous capillary endothelial cell.

What are the primary functions of the respiratory epithelium?

_____

_____

Why doesn't gas exchange occur in bronchi?

_____

What is the primary functional unit of the lung?

_____

The alveolar wall is very delicate and subject to collapse. Why is there no smooth muscle present in its wall for support?

_____

_____

What are the three basic components of the air-blood barrier?

_____

_____

Digestive Tissue Review

From the PhysioEx main menu, select **Histology Review Supplement.** When the screen comes up, click **Select an Image Group.** From Group Listing, click **Digestive Tissue Slides.** To view slides without labels, click the **Labels Off** button at the bottom right of the monitor.

Salivary Gland

The digestive process begins in the mouth with the physical breakdown of food by mastication. At the same time salivary gland secretions moisten the food and begin to hydrolyze carbohydrates. The saliva that enters the mouth is a mix of serous secretions and mucus (mucin) produced by the three major pairs of salivary glands.

Click slide 1.
The **secretory units** of the salivary tissue shown here are composed predominantly of clusters of pale-staining mucus-secreting cells. More darkly stained serous cells cluster to form a **demilune** (half moon) adjacent to the **lumen** and contribute a clear fluid to the salivary secretion. Salivary secretions flow to the mouth from the respective glands through a well-developed **duct** system.

Are salivary glands endocrine or exocrine glands?

_____

Which salivary secretion, mucous or serous, is more thin and watery in consistency?

_____

Esophagus

Through contractions of its muscular wall (peristalsis), the esophagus propels food from the mouth to the stomach. Four major layers are apparent when the wall of the esophagus is cut in transverse section:

Click slide 2.
1. The **mucosa** adjacent to the lumen consists of a nonkeratinized **stratified squamous epithelium,** its immediately subjacent connective tissue (lamina propria) containing blood vessels, nerves, lymphatic vessels, and cells of the immune system, and a thin smooth muscle layer (muscularis mucosa) forms the boundary between the mucosa and the submucosa. Because this slide is a low magnification view, it is not possible to discern all parts of the mucosa nor the boundary between it and the submucosa.

2. The **submucosa** is a layer of connective tissue of variable density, traversed by larger caliber vessels and nerves, that houses the mucus-secreting esophageal **glands** whose secretions protect the epithelium and further lubricate the passing food bolus.

3. Much of the substance of the esophageal wall consists of both circumferentially and longitudinally oriented layers of muscle called the **muscularis externa.** The muscularis externa is composed of skeletal muscle nearest the mouth, smooth muscle nearest the stomach, and a mix of both skeletal and smooth muscle in between.

4. The outermost layer of the esophagus is an adventitia for the portion of the esophagus in the thorax, and a serosa after the esophagus penetrates the diaphragm and enters the abdominal cavity.

Click slide 3.
Here we can see the abrupt change in epithelium at the gastroesophageal junction, where the **esophagus** becomes continuous with the **stomach.**

Briefly explain the difference between an adventitia and a serosa.

_____

_____

Stomach

The wall of the stomach has the same basic four-layered organization as that of the esophagus.

Click slide 4.
The **mucosa** of the stomach consists of a simple columnar epithelium, a thin connective tissue lamina propria, and a thin **muscularis mucosa.** The most significant feature of the stomach mucosa is that the epithelium invaginates deeply into the lamina propria to form superficial **gastric pits** and deeper **gastric glands.** Although the epithelium of the stomach is composed of a variety of cell types, each with a unique and important function, only three are mentioned here (see slide 5).

Click slide 5.
The **surface mucous cells** are simple columnar cells that line the **gastric pits** and secrete mucus continuously onto the surface of the epithelium. The large round pink- to red-stained **parietal cells** that secrete hydrochloric acid (HCl) line the upper half of the gastric glands; more abundant in the lower half of the gastric glands are the chief cells (not shown), usually stained blue, that secrete pepsinogen (a precursor to pepsin).

Click slide 4.
The submucosa is similar to that of the esophagus but without glands. The muscularis externa has the two typical circumferential and longitudinal layers of smooth muscle, plus an extra layer of smooth muscle oriented obliquely. The stomach's outermost layer is a serosa.

What is the function of the mucus secreted by surface mucous cells?

_____

Small Intestine

The key to understanding the histology of the small intestine lies in knowing that its major function is absorption. To that end, its absorptive surface area has been amplified greatly in the following ways:

1. The mucosa and submucosa are thrown into permanent folds (plicae circulares).

2. Fingerlike extensions of the lamina propria form **villi** (singular: **villus**) that protrude into the intestinal lumen *(click slide 7)*.

3. The individual **simple columnar epithelial cells** (enterocytes) that cover the villi have **microvilli** (a **brush border**), tiny projections of apical plasma membrane to increase their absorptive surface area *(click slide 6)*.

Click slide 7.
Although all three segments of the small intestine (duodenum, jejunum, and ileum) possess villi and tubular **crypts** of Lieberkühn that project deep into the mucosa between villi, some unique features are present in particular segments. For example, large mucous glands (duodenal glands, **Brunner's glands**) are present in the submucosa of the duodenum. In addition, permanent aggregates of lymphatic tissue (**Peyer's patches**) are a unique characteristic of the ileum *(click slide 8)*.

Aside from these specific features and the fact that the height of the villi vary from quite tall in the duodenum to fairly short in the terminal ileum, the overall morphology of mucosa, submucosa, muscularis externa, and serosa is quite similar in all three segments.

Why is it important for the duodenum to add large quantities of mucus (from the duodenal glands) to the partially digested food entering it from the stomach?

_____

Colon

Click slide 9.
The four-layered organization is maintained in the wall of the colon, but the colon has no villi, only **crypts** of Lieberkühn. Simple columnar epithelial cells (enterocytes with microvilli) are present to absorb water from the digested food mass, and the numbers of mucous **goblet cells** are increased substantially, especially toward the distal end of the colon.

Why is it important to have an abundance of mucous goblet cells in the colon?

_____

Liver

The functional tissue of the liver is organized into hexagonally shaped cylindrical lobules, each delineated by connective tissue.

Click slide 11.
Within the lobule, large rounded **hepatocytes** form linear cords that radiate peripherally from the center of the lobule at the **central vein** to the surrounding connective tissue. Blood **sinusoids** lined by simple squamous endothelial cells and darkly stained **phagocytic Kupffer cells** are interposed between cords of hepatocytes in the same radiating pattern.

Click slide 10.
Located in the surrounding connective tissue, roughly at the points of the hexagon where three lobules meet, is the **portal triad** (portal canal).

Click slide 12.
The three constituents of the portal triad include a branch of the **hepatic artery,** a branch of the hepatic **portal vein,** and a **bile duct.** Both the hepatic artery and portal vein empty their oxygen-rich blood and nutrient-rich blood, respectively, into the sinusoids. This blood mixes in the sinusoids and flows centrally in between and around the hepatocytes toward the central vein. Bile, produced by hepatocytes, is secreted into very small channels (bile canaliculi) and flows peripherally (away from the central vein) to the bile duct. Thus, the flow of blood is from peripheral to central in a hepatic lobule, while the bile flow is from central to peripheral.

What general type of cell is the phagocytic Kupffer cell?

_____

Blood in the portal vein flows directly from what organs?

_____

What is the function of bile in the digestive process?

_____

Pancreas

Click slide 13.
The exocrine portion of the pancreas synthesizes and secretes pancreatic enzymes. The individual exocrine **secretory unit,** or acinus, is formed by a group of pyramidal-shaped pancreatic acinar cells clustered around a central lumen into which they secrete their products. A system of pancreatic ducts then transports the enzymes to the duodenum where they are added to the lumen contents to further aid digestion. The groups of pale-staining cells are the endocrine pancreatic islet (**islets of Langerhans**) cells.

Renal Tissue Review

From the PhysioEx main menu, select **Histology Review Supplement.** When the screen comes up, click **Select an Image Group.** From Group Listing, click **Renal Tissue Slides.** To view slides without labels, click the **Labels Off** button at the bottom right of the monitor.

The many functions of the kidney include filtration, absorption, and secretion. The kidney filters the blood of metabolic wastes, water, and electrolytes and reabsorbs most of the water and sodium ions filtered to regulate and maintain the body's fluid volume and electrolyte balance. The kidney also plays an endocrine role in secreting compounds that increase blood pressure and stimulate red blood cell production.

The uriniferous tubule is the functional unit of the kidney. It consists of two components: the nephron to filter and the collecting tubules and ducts to carry away the filtrate.

Click slide 1.

The nephron itself consists of the **renal corpuscle,** an intimate association of the glomerular capillaries (**glomerulus**) with the cup-shaped Bowman's capsule, and a single elongated renal tubule consisting of segments regionally and sequentially named the **proximal convoluted tubule (PCT),** the descending and ascending segments of the loop of Henle, and the distal convoluted tubule (DCT).

Click slide 2.

A closer look at the renal corpuscle shows both the simple squamous epithelium of the outer layer (parietal layer) of the glomerular capsule (**Bowman's capsule**) and the specialized inner layer (visceral layer) of **podocytes** that extend footlike processes to completely envelop the capillaries of the renal glomerulus. Processes of adjacent podocytes interdigitate with one another, leaving only small slits (filtration slits) between the processes through which fluid from the blood is filtered. The filtrate then flows into the **urinary space** that is directly continuous with the first segment of the renal tubule, the **PCT.** The PCT is lined by robust cuboidal cells equipped with microvilli to greatly increase the surface area of the side of the cell facing the lumen.

Click slide 3.

In the **loop of Henle,** lining cells are simple squamous to simple cuboidal. The DCT cells are also simple cuboidal but are usually much smaller than those of the PCT. The sparse distribution of microvilli, if present at all, on the cells of the DCT relates to their lesser role in absorption. The DCT is continuous directly with the **collecting tubules** and collecting ducts that drain the filtrate out of the kidney.

The large renal artery and its many subdivisions provide an abundant blood supply to the kidney. The smallest distal branches of the renal artery become the afferent arterioles that directly supply the capillaries of the glomerulus. In a unique situation, blood from the glomerular capillaries passes into the efferent arteriole rather than into a venule. The efferent arteriole then perfuses two more capillary beds, the peritubular capillary bed and vasa recta that provide nutrient blood to the kidney tissue itself, before ultimately draining into the renal venous system.

In which segment of the renal tubule does roughly 75–80% of reabsorption occur?

_____

How are proximal convoluted tubule (PCT) cells similar to enterocytes of the small intestine?

_____

Starting from inside the glomerular capillary through to the urinary space, what are the three layers through which the filtrate must pass?

_____

Under normal circumstances in a healthy individual, would red blood cells or any other cells be present in the renal filtrate?

_____

In addition to providing nutrients to the kidney tubules, what is one other function of the capillaries in the peritubular capillary bed?

_____

Cell Transport Mechanisms and Permeability

Choose all answers that apply to questions 1 and 2, and place their letters on the response blanks to the right.

1. Differential permeability: _____

    a.   is also called selective permeability

    b.   refers to the ability of the plasma membrane to select what passes through it

    c.   implies that all substances pass through membranes without hindrance

    d.   keeps wastes inside the cell and nutrients outside the cell

2. Passive transport includes: _____

    a. osmosis   b. simple diffusion   c. bulk-phase endocytosis   d. pinocytosis   e. facilitated diffusion

3. The following refer to the dialysis simulation.

Did the 20 MWCO membrane exclude any solute(s)? _____

Which solute(s) passed through the 100 MWCO membrane? _____

Which solute exhibited the highest diffusion rate through the 100 MWCO membrane? _____

Explain why this is so. _____

4. The following refer to the facilitated diffusion simulation.

Are substances able to travel against their concentration gradient? _____

Name two ways to increase the rate of glucose transport. _____

Did NaCl affect glucose transport? _____

Does NaCl require a transport protein for diffusion? _____

5. The following refer to the osmosis simulation.

Does osmosis require energy? _____   _____

Is water excluded by any of the dialysis membranes? _____

Is osmotic pressure generated if solutes freely diffuse? _____

Explain how solute concentration affects osmotic pressure. _____

_____   _____

6. The following refer to the filtration simulation.

What does the simulated filtration membrane represent in a living organism? _____

_____

What characteristic of a solute determines whether or not it passes through a filtration membrane?

_____

Would filtration occur if we equalized the pressure on both sides of a filtration membrane? _____

7. The following questions refer to the active transport simulation.

Does the presence of glucose carrier proteins affect Na^+ transport? _____

Can Na^+ be transported against its concentration gradient? _____

Are Na^+ and K^+ transported in the same direction? _____

The ratio of Na^+ to K^+ transport is _____ Na^+ transported out of the cell for every _____ K^+ transported into the cell.

8. What single characteristic of the differentially permeable membranes used in the simple diffusion and filtration experiments

determines which substances pass through them? _____

In addition to this characteristic, what other factors influence the passage of substances through living membranes?

_____

9. Assume the left beaker contains 4 mM NaCl, 9 mM glucose, and 10 mM albumin. The right beaker contains 10 mM NaCl, 10 mM glucose, and 40 mM albumin. Furthermore, the dialysis membrane is permeable to all substances except albumin. State whether the substance will move (a) to the right beaker, (b) to the left beaker, or (c) not move.

Glucose _____   Albumin _____   Water _____   NaCl _____

10. Assume you are conducting the experiment illustrated below. Both hydrochloric acid (HCl; molecular weight of about 36.5) and ammonium hydroxide (NH_4OH; molecular weight of 35) are volatile and easily enter the gaseous state. When they meet, the following reaction will occur:

$$HCl + NH_4OH \rightarrow H_2O + NH_4Cl$$

Ammonium chloride (NH_4Cl) will be deposited on the glass tubing as a smoky precipitate where the two gases meet. Predict which gas will diffuse more quickly, and indicate to which end of the tube the smoky precipitate will be closer.

a.   The faster diffusing gas is _____.

b.   The precipitate forms closer to the _____ end.

Rubber stopper   Cotton wad with HCl   Cotton wad with NH_4OH

Support

11. When food is pickled for human consumption, as much water as possible is removed from the food. What method is used to achieve this dehydrating effect? _____

_____

12. What determines whether a transport process is active or passive? _____

_____

13. Characterize passive and active transport as fully as possible by choosing all the phrases that apply and inserting their letters on the answer blanks.

Passive transport: _____   Active transport: _____

    a.   accounts for the movement of fats and respiratory gases through the plasma membrane

    b.   explains solute pumping, bulk-phase endocytosis, and pinocytosis

    c.   includes osmosis, simple diffusion, and filtration

    d.   may occur against concentration and/or electrical gradients

    e.   uses hydrostatic pressure or molecular energy as the driving force

    f.   moves ions, amino acids, and some sugars across the plasma membrane

14. Define the following terms.

diffusion: _____

_____

osmosis: _____

_____

simple diffusion: _____

_____

filtration: _____

_____

active transport: _____

_____

bulk-phase endocytosis: _____

_____

pinocytosis: _____

_____

facilitated diffusion: _____

_____

Skeletal Muscle Physiology

Electrical Stimulation

1. Complete the following statements by filling in your answers on the appropriate lines below.

A motor unit consists of a __a__ and all the __b__ it innervates. Whole muscle contraction is a(n) __c__ response. In order for muscles to work in a practical sense, __d__ is the method used to produce a slow, steady increase in muscle force. When we see the slightest evidence of force production on a tracing, the stimulus applied must have reached __e__. The weakest stimulation that will elicit the strongest contraction that a muscle is capable of is called the __f__. That level of contraction is called the __g__. When the __h__ of stimulation is so high that the muscle tracing shows fused peaks, __i__ has been achieved.

a. _____

b. _____

c. _____

d. _____

e. _____

f. _____

g. _____

h. _____

i. _____

2. Name each phase of a typical muscle twitch, and, on the following line, describe what is happening in each phase.

a. _____

_____

b. _____

_____

c. _____

_____

3. Explain how the PhysioEx experimental muscle stimulation differs from the in vivo stimulation via the nervous system. (Note that the graded muscle response following both stimulation methods is similar.)

_____

_____

_____

4. What are the two *experimental* ways in which mode of stimulation can affect the muscle force?

_____ and _____

Explain your answer.

_____

_____

_____

Isometric Contraction

5. Identify the following conditions by choosing one of the key terms listed on the right.

Key:

_____ is generated by muscle tissue when it is being stretched

a.   Total force

_____ requires the input of energy

b.   Resting force

_____ is measured by recording instrumentation during contraction

c.   Active force

6. Circle the correct response in the parentheses for each statement.

An increase in resting length results in a(n) (increase / decrease) in passive force.

The active force initially (increased / decreased) and then (increased / decreased) as the resting length was increased from minimum to maximum.

As the total force increased, the active force (increased / decreased).

7. Explain what happens to muscle force production at extremes of length (too short or too long). (Hint: Think about sarcomere structure.)

Muscle too short: _____

_____

Muscle too long: _____

_____

Isotonic Contraction

8. Assuming a fixed starting length, describe the effect resistance has on the initial velocity of shortening, and explain why it has this effect.

_____

_____

_____

9. A muscle has just been stimulated under conditions that will allow both isometric and isotonic contractions. Describe what is happening in terms of length and force.

Isometric: _____

_____

Isotonic: _____

_____

Terms

10. Select the condition from column B that most correctly identifies the term in column A.

Column A		Column B
_____ 1. muscle twitch	a.	many cells responding to one neuron
_____ 2. wave summation	b.	affects the force a muscle can generate
_____ 3. multiple motor unit summation	c.	a single contraction of intact muscle
_____ 4. resting length	d.	recruitment
_____ 5. resistance	e.	increasing force produced by increasing stimulus frequency
_____ 6. initial velocity of shortening	f.	muscle length changing due to relaxation
_____ 7. isotonic shortening	g.	caused by application of maximal stimulus
_____ 8. isotonic lengthening	h.	weight
_____ 9. motor unit	i.	exhibits graded response
_____ 10. whole muscle	j.	high values with low resistance values
_____ 11. tetanus	k.	changing muscle length due to active forces
_____ 12. maximal response	l.	recording shows no evidence of muscle relaxation

Neurophysiology of Nerve Impulses

The Nerve Impulse

1. Match each of the terms in column B with the appropriate definition in column A.

Column A

_____ 1. term used to denote that a membrane potential is sitting at about −70 mV

_____ 2. reversal of membrane potential due to influx of sodium ions

_____ 3. major cation found outside the cell

_____ 4. minimal stimulus needed to elicit an action potential

_____ 5. period when cell membrane is totally insensitive to additional stimuli, regardless of the stimulus force used

_____ 6. major cation found inside the cell

Column B

a. threshold

b. sodium

c. potassium

d. resting membrane potential

e. absolute refractory period

f. depolarization

2. Fill in the blanks with the correct words or terms.

Neurons, as with other excitable cells of the body, have two major physiological properties: _____ and

_____. A neuron has a positive charge on the outer surface of the cell membrane due in part to the

action of an active transport system called the _____. This system moves

_____ out of the cell and _____ into the cell. The inside of the cell membrane will

be negative, not only due to the active transport system but also because of _____, which remain
negative due to intracellular pH and keep the inside of the cell membrane negative.

3. Why don't the terms *depolarization* and *action potential* mean the same thing?

_____

_____

_____

4. What is the difference between membrane irritability and membrane conductivity?

_____

_____

_____

Eliciting a Nerve Impulse

5. Why does the nerve action potential increase slightly when you add 1.0 V to the threshold voltage and stimulate the nerve?

_____

_____

_____

6. If you were to spend a lot of time studying nerve physiology in the laboratory, what type of stimulus would you use and why?

_____

_____

_____

7. Why does the addition of sodium chloride elicit an action potential? _____

_____

_____

Inhibiting a Nerve Impulse

8. What was the effect of ether on eliciting an action potential? _____

_____

9. Does the addition of ether to the nerve cause any permanent alteration in neural response?

_____

10. What was the effect of curare on eliciting an action potential?

_____

11. Explain the reason for your answer to question 10 above.

_____

12. What was the effect of lidocaine on eliciting an action potential?

_____

Nerve Conduction Velocity

13. What is the relationship between size of the nerve and conduction velocity? _____

_____

_____

14. Keeping your answer to question 13 in mind, how might you draw an analogy between the nerves in the human body and electrical wires?

_____

15. Hypothesize what types of animals would have the fastest conduction velocities.

_____

16. How does myelination affect nerve conduction velocity? Explain. _____

_____

_____

_____

17. If any of the nerves used were reversed in their placement on the stimulating and recording electrodes, would any differences be seen in conduction velocity? Explain.

_____

_____

_____

Endocrine System Physiology

1. In the following columns, match the hormone on the left with its source on the right.

    _____ thyroxine   a.   ovary

    _____ estrogen   b.   thyroid gland

    _____ thyroid-stimulating hormone (TSH)   c.   pancreas

    _____ insulin   d.   pituitary gland

2. Each hormone is known to have a specific target tissue. For each hormone listed, identify its target tissue and its specific action.

    thyroxine: _____

    estrogen: _____

    thyroid-stimulating hormone (TSH): _____

    insulin: _____

    follicle-stimulating hormone (FSH): _____

    _____

Metabolism

3. In the metabolism experiment, what was the effect of thyroxine on the overall metabolic rate of the animals?

    _____

    _____

4. Using the respirometer-manometer, you observed the amount of oxygen being used by animals in a closed chamber. What happened to the carbon dioxide the animals produced while in the chamber?

    _____

    _____

5. If the experimental animals in the chamber were engaged in physical activity (such as running in a wheel), how do you think this would change the results of the metabolism experiment?

_____

What changes would you expect to see in the fluid levels of the manometer? _____

_____

6. Why didn't the administration of thyroid-stimulating hormone (TSH) have any effect on the metabolic rate of the thyroidectomized rat? _____

_____

7. Why didn't the administration of propylthiouracil have any effect on the metabolic rate of either the thyroidectomized rat or the hypophysectomized rat? _____

_____

Hormone Replacement Therapy

8. In the experiment with hormone replacement therapy, what was the effect of removing the ovaries from the animals?

_____

_____

9. Specifically, what hormone did the ovariectomies effectively remove from the animals, and what purpose does this hormone serve? _____

_____

10. If a hormone such as testosterone were used in place of estrogen, would any effect be seen? Explain your answer.

_____

_____

11. In the experiment, you administered seven injections of estrogen to the experimental rat over the course of seven days. What do you think would happen if you administered one injection of estrogen per day for an additional week?

_____

_____

12. What do you think would happen if you administered seven injections of estrogen to the experimental rat all in one day?

_____

13. In a wet lab, why would you need to wait several weeks after the animals received their ovariectomies before you could perform this experiment on them? _____

_____

Insulin and Diabetes

14. In the insulin and diabetes experiment, what was the effect of administering alloxan to the experimental animal?

_____

15. When insulin travels to the cells of the body, the concentration of what compound will elevate within the cells?

_____

What is the specific action of this compound, within the cells? _____

_____

16. Name the diseases described below:

a. the condition when insulin is not produced by the pancreas: _____

b. the condition when insulin is produced by the pancreas, but the body fails to respond to the insulin:

_____

17. What was the effect of administering insulin to the diabetic rat? _____

_____

18. What is a glucose standard curve, and why did you need to obtain one for this experiment? _____

_____

19. Would altering the light wavelength of the spectrophotometer have any bearing on the results obtained? Explain your answer. _____

_____

20. What would you do to help a friend who had inadvertently taken an overdose of insulin? Why should your solution be beneficial? _____

Cardiovascular Dynamics

For questions 1 and 2 below, choose all answers that apply and place their letters on the response blanks to the right of the statement.

1. The circulation of blood through the vascular system is influenced by ____ _____.

   a. blood viscosity
   b. the length of blood vessels

   c. the driving pressure behind the blood
   d. the radius or diameter of blood vessels

2. Peripheral resistance depends on _____.

   a. blood viscosity
   b. blood pressure

   c. vessel length
   d. vessel radius

3. Complete the following statements.

   The volume of blood remaining in the heart after ventricular contraction is called the _____.

   Cardiac output is defined as _____.

   The amount of blood pumped by the heart in a single beat is called the _____ volume.

   The human heart is actually two individual pumps working in _ _____.

   Stroke volume is calculated by _____.

   If stroke volume decreased, heart rate would _____ in order to maintain blood flow.

4. How could the heart compensate to maintain proper blood flow for the following conditions?

   High peripheral resistance: _____

   A leaky atrioventricular valve: _____

   A constricted semilunar valve: _____

5. How does the size of the heart change under conditions of chronic high peripheral resistance?

   _____

6. The following questions refer to the Vessel Resistance experiment.

   How was the flow rate affected when the radius of the flow tube was increased? _____

   Which of the adjustable parameters had the greatest effect on fluid flow? _____

   How does vessel length affect fluid flow? _____

If you increased fluid viscosity, what parameter(s) could you adjust to keep fluid flow constant?

_____

Explain your answer. _____

_____

If the driving pressure in the left beaker was 100 mm Hg, how could you adjust the conditions of the experiment to com-

pletely stop fluid flow? _____

7. The following questions refer to the Pump Mechanics experiment.

What would happen if the right side of the heart pumped faster than the left side of the heart?

_____

_____

When you change the radius of the right flow tube in Pump Mechanics, the resulting plot looks different than the radius plot in the Vessel Resistance experiment. How would the plot look if you changed the radius of both flow tubes in Pump Mechanics instead of just the right flow tube?

_____

_____

Why are valves needed in the Pump Mechanics equipment? _____

What happens to blood flow if peripheral resistance equals pump pressure? _____

Theoretically, what would happen to the pumping ability of the heart if the end systolic volume was equal to the end dia-

stolic volume? _____

8. Match the part in the simulation equipment to the analogous cardiac structure or physiological term listed in the key below.

Simulation Equipment:

_____ 1. valve leading to the right beaker

_____ 2. valve leading to the pump

_____ 3. left flow tube

_____ 4. right flow tube

_____ 5. pump end volume

_____ 6. pump starting volume

_____ 7. pressure in the right beaker

_____ 8. pressure in the left beaker

_____ 9. pump pressure

Key:

a. pulmonary veins

b. bicuspid valve

c. ventricular filling pressure

d. peripheral resistance

e. aortic valve

f. end diastolic volume

g. aorta

h. end systolic volume

i. systolic pressure

9. Define the following terms.

blood flow: _____

_____

peripheral resistance: _____

_____

viscosity: _____

_____

radius: _____

_____

end diastolic volume: _____

_____

systole: _____

_____

diastole: _____

_____

Frog Cardiovascular Physiology

Special Electrical Properties of Cardiac Muscle: Automaticity and Rhythmicity

1. Define the following terms.

    automaticity: _____

    rhythmicity: _____

2. Explain the anatomical differences between frog and human hearts.

    _____

    _____

    _____

Baseline Frog Heart Activity

3. Define the following terms.

    intrinsic heart control: _____

    extrinsic heart control: _____

4. Why is it necessary to keep the frog heart moistened with Ringer's solution? _____

    _____

Refractory Period of Cardiac Muscle

5. Define *extrasystole.* _____

    _____

6. Refer to the exercise to answer the following questions.

    What was the effect of stimulating the heart during ventricular contraction? _____

    During ventricular relaxation? _____

    During the pause interval? _____

    What does this information indicate about the refractory period of cardiac muscle?

    _____

    Can cardiac muscle be tetanized? _____ Why or why not? _____

The Effect of Vagus Nerve Stimulation

7. What was the effect of vagal stimulation on heart rate? _____.

8. What is vagal escape? _____

9. Why is the vagal escape valuable in maintaining homeostasis? _____

_____

Physical and Chemical Modifiers of Heart Rate

10. Describe the effect of thermal factors on the frog heart.

Cold: _____ Heat: _____

11. Which of the following factors caused the same, or very similar, heart rate–reducing effects: epinephrine, atropine, pilo-carpine, digitalis, and/or potassium ions.

_____

_____

Which of the factors listed above would reverse or antagonize vagal effects? _____

_____

12. Did administering any of the following produce any changes in force of contraction (shown by peaks of increasing or decreasing height)? If so, explain the mechanism.

Epinephrine: _____

_____

Calcium ions: _____

_____

13. Excessive amounts of each of the following ions would most likely interfere with normal heart activity. Explain the type of changes caused in each case.

K^+: _____

Ca^{2+}: _____

Na^+: _____

14. Define the following terms.

parasympathomimetic: _____

ectopic pacemaker: _____

15. Explain how digitalis works. _____

_____

Respiratory System Mechanics

Define the following terms.

1. *ventilation:* _____

2. *inspiration:* _____

3. *expiration:* _____

Measuring Respiratory Volumes

4. Write the respiratory volume term and the normal value that is described by the following statements.

Volume of air present in the lungs after a forceful expiration: _____

Volume of air that can be expired forcefully after a normal expiration: _____

Volume of air that is breathed in and out during a normal respiration: _____

Volume of air that can be inspired forcefully after a normal inspiration: _____

Volume of air corresponding to TV + IRV + ERV: _____

5. Fill in the formula for minute respiratory volume.

_____

Examining the Effect of Changing Airway Resistance on Respiratory Volumes

6. Even though pulmonary function tests are not diagnostic, they can help determine the difference between

_____ and _____ disorders.

7. Chronic bronchitis and asthma are examples of _____ disorders.

8. Describe FEV_1. _____

_____

9. Explain the difference between FVC and FEV_1. _____

_____

10. What effect would increasing airway resistance have on FEV_1? _____

Examining the Effect of Surfactant

11. Explain the term *surface tension*. _____

_____

12. Surfactant is a detergent-like _____.

13. How does surfactant work? _____

14. What might happen to ventilation if the watery film lining the alveoli did not contain surfactant?

_____

Investigating Intrapleural Pressure

15. Complete the following statements.

The pressure within the pleural cavity, __1__, is __2__ than the pressure within the alveoli. This __3__ pressure condition is caused by two forces, the tendency of the lung to recoil due to its __4__ properties and the __5__ of the alveolar fluid. These two forces act to pull the lungs away from the thoracic wall, creating a partial __6__ in the pleural cavity. Because the pressure in the __7__ space is lower than __8__, any opening created in the thoracic wall equalizes the intrapleural pressure with the atmospheric pressure, allowing air to enter the pleural cavity, a condition called __9__. Pneumothorax allows __10__, a condition called __11__.

1. _____

2. _____

3. _____

4. _____

5. _____

6. _____

7. _____

8. _____

9. _____

10. _____

11. _____

16. Why is the intrapleural pressure negative rather than positive?_____

_____

_____

17. Would intrapleural pressure be positive or negative when blowing up a balloon? Explain your answer.

_____

_____

Exploring Various Breathing Patterns

18. Match the term listed in column B with the descriptive phrase in column A. (There may be more than one correct answer.)

Column A

_____1. causes a drop in carbon dioxide concentration in the blood

_____2. results in lower blood pH

_____3. stimulates an increased respiratory rate

_____4. results in a lower respiratory rate

_____5. can be considered an extreme form of rebreathing

_____6. causes a rise in blood carbon dioxide

Column B

a. rebreathing

b. rapid breathing

c. breath holding

19. Because carbon dioxide is the main stimulus for respirations, what would happen to respiratory drive if you held your

breath? _____

_____

Chemical and Physical Processes of Digestion

Chemical Digestion of Foodstuffs: Enzymatic Action

1. Match the following definitions with the proper choices from the key.

   Key: a.   catalyst   b.   control   c.   enzyme   d.   substrate

   _____ 1.   increases the rate of a chemical reaction without becoming part of the product

   _____ 2.   provides a standard of comparison for test results

   _____ 3.   biological catalyst; protein in nature

   _____ 4.   substance on which an enzyme works

2. Name three characteristics of enzymes. _____

   _____

3. Explain the following statement: The enzymes of the digestive system are classified as hydrolases.

   _____

   _____

4. Fill in the chart below with what you have learned about the various digestive system enzymes encountered in this exercise.

Enzyme	Organ producing it	Site of action	Substrate(s)	Optimal pH
Salivary amylase				
Pepsin				
Lipase (pancreatic)				

5. Name the end products of digestion for the following types of foods.

   Proteins: _____   Carbohydrates: _____

   Fats: _____ and _____

6. You used several different indicators or tests in the laboratory to determine the presence or absence of certain substances. Choose the correct test or indicator from the key to correspond to the condition described below.

   Key: a. IKI   b. Benedict's solution   c. pH meter   d. BAPNA

   _____ 1. used to test for protein hydrolysis, which was indicated by a yellow color

   _____ 2. used to test for the presence of starch, which was indicated by a blue-black color

   _____ 3. used to test for the presence of fatty acids

   _____ 4. used to test for the presence of a reducing sugar (such as maltose), which was indicated by a blue to green (or to rust) color change

7. The three-dimensional structure of a functional protein is altered by intense heat or nonphysiological pH even though peptide bonds may not break. Such a change in protein structure is called denaturation, and denatured enzymes are not functional. Explain why.

   _____

   _____

8. What experimental conditions in the simulation resulted in denatured enzymes? _____

   _____

9. Complete the mechanism of absorption section in the chart below for each of the substances listed. Use a check mark to indicate whether the absorption would result in the movement of a substance into the blood capillaries or the lymph capillaries (lacteals).

Substance	Mechanism of absorption	Blood	Lymph
Monosaccharides			
Fatty acids and glycerol			
Amino acids			

10. Imagine that you have been chewing a piece of bread for 5 to 6 minutes. How would you expect its taste to change during

    this time? _____

11. People on a strict diet to lose weight begin to metabolize stored fats at an accelerated rate. How could this condition affect

    blood pH? _____

Starch Digestion by Salivary Amylase

12. What conclusions can you draw when an experimental sample gives both a positive starch test and a positive maltose test?

_____

13. Why was 37°C the optimal incubation temperature? _____

_____

14. Why did very little, if any, starch digestion occur in tube 1? _____

15. Why did very little starch digestion occur in tubes 6 and 7? _____

16. Imagine that you have told a group of your peers that amylase is capable of digesting starch to maltose. If you had not run the experiment in control tubes 3, 4, and 5, what objections to your statement could be raised?

_____

_____

Assessing Cellulose Digestion

17. What is the effect of freezing on enzyme activity?

_____

18. What can you conclude about the ability of salivary amylase to digest cellulose?

_____

19. What can you conclude about the ability of bacteria to digest cellulose?

_____

Protein Digestion by Pepsin

20. Why is an indicator reagent such as IKI or Benedict's solution not necessary when using a substrate like BAPNA?

_____

21. Trypsin is a pancreatic hydrolase present in the small intestine during digestion. Would trypsin work well in the stomach?

_____ Explain your answer. _____

_____

22. How does the optical density of a solution containing BAPNA relate to enzyme activity? _____

_____

23. What happens to pepsin activity as it reaches the small intestine? _____

Fat Digestion by Pancreatic Lipase and the Action of Bile

24. Why does the pH of a fatty solution decrease as enzymatic hydrolysis increases? _____

_____

25. How does bile affect fat digestion? _____

26. Why is it not possible to determine the activity of lipase in the pH 2.0 buffer using the pH meter assay method?

_____

27. Why is bile not considered an enzyme? _____

Physical Processes: Mechanisms of Food Propulsion and Mixing

28. Complete the following statements. Write your answers in the numbered spaces below.

Swallowing, or __1__, occurs in two phases—the __2__ and __3__. One of these phases, the __4__ phase, is voluntary. During the voluntary phase, the __5__ is used to push the food into the back of the throat. During swallowing, the __6__ rises to ensure that its passageway is covered by the epiglottis so that the ingested substances do not enter the respiratory passageways. It is possible to swallow water while standing on your head because the water is carried along the esophagus involuntarily by the process of __7__. The pressure exerted by the foodstuffs on the __8__ sphincter causes it to open, allowing the food to enter the stomach.

The two major types of propulsive movements that occur in the small intestine are __9__ and __10__. One of these movements, __11__, acts to continually mix the foods and to increase the absorption rate by moving different parts of the chyme mass over the intestinal mucosa, but it has less of a role in moving foods along the digestive tract.

1. _____   7. _____

2. _____   8. _____

3. _____   9. _____

4. _____   10. _____

5. _____   11. _____

6. _____

Renal System Physiology

Define the following terms.

1. *glomerulus:* _____

2. *renal tubule:* _____

3. *glomerular capsule:* _____

4. *renal corpuscle:* _____

5. *afferent arteriole:* _____

6. *efferent arteriole:* _____

Investigating the Effect of Flow Tube Radius on Glomerular Filtration

7. In terms of the blood supply to and from the glomerulus, explain why the glomerular capillary bed is unusual.

_____

_____

8. How would pressure in the glomerulus be affected by constricting the afferent arteriole? Explain your answer.

_____

_____

9. How would pressure in the glomerulus be affected by constricting the efferent arteriole? Explain your answer.

_____

_____

Assessing Combined Effects on Glomerular Filtration

10. If systemic blood pressure started to rise, what could the arterioles of the glomerulus do to keep glomerular filtration rate

constant? _____

_____

11. One of the experiments you performed in the simulation was to close the valve at the end of the collecting duct. Is closing that valve more like constricting an afferent arteriole or more like a kidney stone? Explain your answer.

_____

_____

12. Constricting the efferent arteriole would have the same effect on glomerular filtration as (constricting / dilating) the afferent arteriole.

_____

_____

Exploring the Role of the Solute Gradient on Maximum Urine Concentration Achievable

13. Complete the following statements.

In the process of urine formation, solutes and water move from the __1__ of the nephron into the __2__ spaces. The passive movement of solutes and water from the lumen of the renal tubule into the interstitial spaces relies in part on the __3__ surrounding the nephron. When the nephron is permeable to solutes or water, __4__ will be reached between the interstitial fluid and the contents of the nephron. __5__ is a hormone that increases the water permeability of the __6__ and the collecting duct, allowing water to flow to areas of higher solute concentration, usually from the lumen of the nephron into the surrounding interstitial area. __7__ is a hormone that causes __8__ reabsorption at the expense of __9__ loss into the lumen of the tubule.

1. _____

2. _____

3. _____

4. _____

5. _____

6. _____

7. _____

8. _____

9. _____

14. Would the passive movement of substances occur if the interstitial solute concentration was the same as the filtrate solute concentration? Explain your answer.

_____

_____

Studying the Effect of Glucose Carrier Proteins on Glucose Reabsorption

15. In terms of the function of the nephron, explain why one might find glucose in the urine exiting the collecting duct.

_____

_____

16. Imagine this scenario: a person has the normal number of glucose carriers in the nephrons yet has glucose in the urine. What could be the cause of this condition? (Hint: think about filtration rate.)

_____

_____

Testing the Effect of Hormones on Urine Formation

17. Complete the following statements.

      The concentration of the __1__ excreted by our kidneys changes, depending on our immediate needs. For example, if a person consumes a large quantity of water, the excess water will be eliminated, producing __2__ urine. On the other hand, under conditions of dehydration, there is a clear benefit to being able to produce urine as __3__ as possible, thereby retaining precious water. Although the medullary gradient makes it possible to excrete concentrated urine, urine dilution or concentration is ultimately under __4__ control. In this experiment, you will investigate the effects of two different hormones on renal function, aldosterone produced by the __5__ and ADH manufactured by the __6__ and stored in the __7__. Aldosterone works to reabsorb __8__ (and thereby water) at the expense of losing __9__. Its site of action is the __10__. ADH makes the distal tubule and collecting duct more permeable to __11__, thereby allowing the body to reabsorb more water from the filtrate when it is present.

1. _____
2. _____
3. _____
4. _____
5. _____
6. _____
7. _____
8. _____
9. _____
10. _____
11. _____

18. Match the term listed in column B with the descriptive phrase in column A. (There may be more than one correct answer.)

Column A	Column B
_____1. causes production of dilute urine	a. increased ADH
_____2. results in increased sodium loss	b. increased aldosterone
_____3. causes the body to retain more potassium	c. decreased ADH
_____4. will cause water retention due to sodium movement	d. decreased aldosterone
_____5. causes water reabsorption due to increased membrane permeability	
_____6. increases sodium reabsorption	

Acid/Base Balance

1. Match each of the terms in column A with the appropriate description in column B.

Column A	Column B
_____ 1. pH	a. condition in which the human body's pH levels fall below 7.35
_____ 2. acid	b. condition in which the human body's pH levels rise above 7.45
_____ 3. base	c. mixes with water in the blood to form carbonic acid
_____ 4. acidosis	d. substance that binds to H^+ in solution
_____ 5. alkalosis	e. substance that releases H^+ in solution
_____ 6. carbon dioxide	f. term used to denote H^+ concentration in body fluids

2. What is the normal range of pH levels of blood and tissue fluids in the human body?

_____

3. What is the difference between a strong acid and a weak acid?

_____

4. What is the difference between a strong base and a weak base?

_____

5. What is the difference between respiratory acidosis/alkalosis and metabolic acidosis/alkalosis?

_____

_____

6. What are the body's two major physiological buffer systems for compensating for acid-base imbalances?

_____ and ____ _____

Respiratory Acidosis and Alkalosis

7. What are some of the causes of respiratory acidosis?

_____

8. What are some of the causes of respiratory alkalosis?

_____

9. What happens to blood pH levels during hyperventilation? Why?

_____

10. What happens to blood pH levels during rebreathing? Why?

_____

_____

11. Circle the correct terms in parentheses.

As respiration increases, P_{CO_2} levels (increase / decrease) and pH levels (rise / fall).

As respiration decreases, P_{CO_2} levels (increase / decrease) and pH levels (rise / fall).

Renal Compensation

12. How does the renal system compensate for conditions of respiratory acidosis?

_____

13. How does the renal system compensate for conditions of respiratory alkalosis?

_____

Metabolic Acidosis and Alkalosis

14. What are some of the causes of metabolic acidosis?

_____

15. What are some of the causes of metabolic alkalosis?

_____

16. Explain how the respiratory system compensates for metabolic acidosis and alkalosis.

_____

_____

_____

17. Explain how the renal system compensates for metabolic acidosis and alkalosis.

_____

_____

_____

18. Circle the correct terms in parentheses.

As metabolic rate increases, respiration (increases / decreases), P_{CO_2} levels (increase / decrease), and pH levels (rise / fall).

As metabolic rate decreases, respiration (increases / decreases), P_{CO_2} levels (increase / decrease), and pH levels (rise / fall).

Blood Analysis

Hematocrit Determination

1. Hematocrit values are usually (higher / lower) in healthy males, compared to healthy females.

   Give one possible explanation for this. _____

   _____

2. Living at high elevations will cause a person's hematocrit to (increase / decrease).

   Explain your answer. _____

   _____

3. Long-term athletic training will cause a person's hematocrit to (increase / decrease).

4. What is anemia? _____

5. Anemia will cause a person's hematocrit to (increase / decrease).

6. Pernicious anemia is due to a lack of vitamin _____

7. How does deficiency of intrinsic factor lead to pernicious anemia? _____

   _____

8. Why would a diet deficient in iron lead to anemia? _____

   _____

9. Which hormone, secreted by the kidney, is responsible for increased production of red blood cells?

   _____

Erythrocyte Sedimentation Rate (ESR)

10. Sickled red blood cells have an abnormal shape and do not tend to form stacks of cells (rouleaux formation). This would (increase / decrease) the sedimentation rate.

11. Is the ESR test a specific test used to diagnose a disease? _____

12. The blood of a cancer patient undergoing chemotherapy is given an ESR test. The results show a slower ESR from the previous month. What might this indicate about the patient's disease?

_____

13. How can the ESR be useful in the evaluation of a patient complaining of chest pains?

_____

14. How can the ESR be useful in the evaluation of a female patient suffering from severe abdominal pains?

_____

Hemoglobin Determination

15. What is the value, in terms of grams of hemoglobin per 100 milliliters of blood, for the following:

a. healthy male: _____

b. healthy female: _____

c. male with polycythemia: _____

d. female with iron deficiency anemia: _____

16. Explain your answer to (c) above. _____

_____

17. Explain your answer to (d) above. _____

18. Complete the following questions to describe hemoglobin.

How many polypeptide chains form the globin portion of the molecule? _____

Each heme group contains an atom of the element _____.

How many heme groups are contained in one molecule of hemoglobin? _____

Each hemoglobin molecule can transport _____ molecules of oxygen.

What color is oxyhemoglobin? _____

19. Hemoglobin values rise in COPD (chronic obstructive pulmonary disease). Give a possible explanation for this.

_____

_____

20. Hemoglobin values decrease in renal disease. Give a possible explanation for this.

_____

_____

Blood Typing

21. Define the following terms.

agglutinogen: _____

agglutinen: _____

gene allele: _____

22. What is the most common ABO blood type in the United States? _____

23. What is the least common ABO blood type in the United States? _____

24. Most Americans are Rh (positive / negative).

25. *Erythroblastosis fetalis* is an uncommon condition in newborn infants. In this condition, the baby is Rh (positive / negative) and the mother is Rh (positive / negative).

26. If your blood agglutinates with both anti-A and anti-B sera, your blood type is _____.

27. If you have type O blood, which antigens are present on your red blood cells?

_____

Which antibodies are present in your plasma? _____

28. Blood type O is considered to be the universal donor type. However, if type O blood is transfused into a person with blood

type B, which of the following is important to remember? _____

a. Use the entire pint of type O blood for the transfusion
b. Separate the type O blood into packed cells and plasma, and use only the packed cells for the transfusion
c. Separate the type O blood into packed cells and plasma, and use only the plasma for the transfusion

Total Blood Cholesterol Determination

29. Cholesterol is an essential factor in homeostasis. Name four uses that the human body has for cholesterol.

a. _____

b. _____

c. _____

d. _____

30. Most of the cholesterol that your body needs is made by what organ? _____

31. High blood cholesterol levels are above _____ mg/100 ml of blood.

32. What is atherosclerosis? _____

33. What is the connection between high blood cholesterol levels and atherosclerosis?

_____

34. What are lipoproteins? _____

35. Low density lipoproteins (LDLs) transport cholesterol to _____

_____.

36. High density lipoproteins (HDLs) transport cholesterol from the _____ to the _____,

where it is broken down and becomes part of bile.

37. Cigarette smoking, stress, and coffee drinking increase levels of _____, or "bad cholesterol."

38. Regular aerobic exercise increases levels of _____, or "good cholesterol."

Serological Testing

1. Match the term on the left with the description on the right.

    Key:　　a.　antigen　　b.　antibody　　c.　serum　　d.　antigenic determinant

    _____ 1.　epitope

    _____ 2.　foreign or "non-self"

    _____ 3.　immunoglobulin, created by plasma cells

    _____ 4.　the fluid portion of the blood with the clotting factors removed

2. Why are there a number of washing steps in serological tests?

    _____

    _____

    _____

3. Describe how you would know that you had a "false positive" result. What does this mean for the rest of your results?

    _____

    _____

    _____

4. Describe how you would know that you had a "false negative" result. What does this mean for the rest of your results?

    _____

    _____

    _____

Direct Fluorescent Antibody Technique

5. Why is this technique a direct method?

    _____

    _____

6. What are elementary bodies and how do they look under the fluorescent microscope?

_____

_____

_____

7. What do you think would happen if you did not fix the sample to the slide with 95% ethyl alcohol?

_____

_____

_____

8. Which patient(s) tested positive for Chlamydia?

_____

9. Was there any non-specific binding for any of the samples? Explain.

_____

_____

Ouchterlony Technique

10. What is a precipitin line?

_____

_____

_____

11. What is the unknown antigen in the simulation?

_____

12. Based upon the results, do you think that human serum albumin and bovine serum albumin have epitopes in common? Explain.

_____

_____

13. What is the process resulting in antigen and antibody moving toward each other?

_____

Enzyme-Linked Immunosorbent Assay

14. In the "sandwich" analogy of the direct ELISA, what is the "bread"?

_____

What is the filling? _____

15. Describe some advantages of using the ELISA technique to process a large number of samples.

_____

_____

_____

_____

16. Which patient(s) were positive for HIV?

_____

17. Describe what would happen if you skipped the step where the developing buffer was added.

_____

_____

_____

_____

Western Blotting Technique

18. The Western blot technique is used as the confirmatory test for a positive ELISA result because it provides better specificity. How does this technique provide better specificity?

_____

_____

_____

19. If a patient tests positive for HIV using the ELISA test but negative using Western blotting, what can you say about the initial ELISA result?

_____

20. Describe the role of the developing buffer in the Western blotting technique.

_____

_____

_____

21. Using the choices listed below, decide which of the criteria apply to the indirect ELISA, which apply to Western Blotting technique, and which apply to both. Use "E" if it applies to ELISA, "W" for Western Blotting, and "B" for both.

Criteria:

_____ 1. It tests for the presence of antibodies in the patient sample.

_____ 2. Electrophoresis is used.

_____ 3. Substrates that change from colorless to colored are used.

_____ 4. An enzyme-linked secondary antibody is used.

_____ 5. Antibodies against individual antigens are detected.

_____ 6. The reaction takes place in a well in a microtiter plate.

_____ 7. An antigen-antibody reaction is detected.

_____ 8. An optical density is read to determine whether or not a sample is positive.